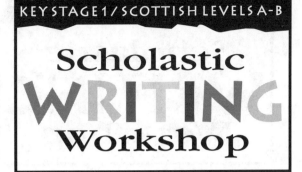

IMAGINATIVE WRITING
KEY STAGE 1 / SCOTTISH LEVELS A–B

Scholastic
WRITING
Workshop

Story
PROJECTS

SUE ELLIS,
ANNE HUGHES
& LYNDA KEITH

Published by Scholastic Ltd,
Villiers House,
Clarendon Avenue,
Leamington Spa,
Warwickshire CV32 5PR.
Text © 1996 Sue Ellis, Anne Hughes and Lynda Keith
© 1996 Scholastic Ltd

34567890   8901234

Project Consultants
Sue Ellis and Gill Friel

Authors
Sue Ellis, Anne Hughes and Lynda Keith

Editor
Clare Gallaher

Assistant Editor
Kate Pearce

Series Designer
Joy White

Designer
Toby Long

Illustrations
Peter Utton

Cover illustration
David Parkins
(From *Blooming Cats* by David R. Morgan, Hippo Books)

Designed using Aldus Pagemaker

British Library Cataloguing-in-Publication Data
A catalogue record for this book is available from the British Library.

ISBN 0-590-53471-8

Contents

5 Chapter One
INTRODUCTION

13 Chapter Two
ASSESSMENT

19 Chapter Three
THE SPIDER'S SHOES

33 Chapter Four
MY FAVOURITE TOY

43 Chapter Five
THE TEDDY BEAR WHO CAME TO SCHOOL

59 Chapter Six
THE MAGICAL TRAVEL MACHINE

71 Chapter Seven
OH NO, BABY!

87 Chapter Eight
ZIGZAG ROBOTS

95 Chapter Nine
THIS IS ME AND THIS IS WHAT I'M LIKE

105 Chapter Ten
HOLIDAY SNAPS

113 Chapter Eleven
OUR HOUSE IS A VERY NICE HOUSE, BUT ONE DAY...

123 Chapter Twelve
NO PLACE LIKE HOME

135 Chapter Thirteen
BIG BOX DENS

139 Chapter Fourteen
MEET MY MONSTER

Scholastic
WRITING
Workshop

Chapter One

INTRODUCTION

TEACHING IMAGINATIVE WRITING

I want teachers to delight in what youngsters do... I want teachers to have a wonderful time watching and admiring and working with young writers.
(Lucy Calkins, *The Art of Teaching Writing*)

This resource has been developed for teachers who want to ensure that the imaginative writing requirements of the National Curricula for England and Wales and for Northern Ireland and the Language 5–14 Guidelines for Scotland are met. It has been produced in the belief that:

• *Children motivate themselves to write.* When teachers create the classroom conditions in which children can use ideas and storytelling skills developed with others and in play, the writing is fun and satisfying. Children want to write their stories.

• *Teachers must foster children's belief in themselves as storytellers and writers.* When children know that their stories are important, they are confident, take pride in their work and have a clear sense of their own voice. Extended writing projects, in which children live the process from initial ideas through to seeing their story read by others, provide a powerful way to ensure that children feel and act like writers.

• *Teachers must understand writing and the support children require.* Teachers must be familiar with specific techniques and strategies that writers use and encourage children to use them also. They must plan the sequence, structure and pacing of writing projects and the organisation and management of lessons to support children. They must be observant and

skilled in working with children and know when activities, play or discussion will help and when children need to concentrate and write alone.

• *Teachers must focus on the writer, not the product.* Teachers who are sensitive to children's needs as writers are observant and analytical of both the writing and the writer. They know, however, that only the child may choose to apply the specific skills and strategies they teach. Effective teaching must therefore focus on the child and explore why and how children make the choices they do.

The importance of storytelling

The urge to tell stories about our lives is uniquely human. From the earliest age, children make up stories about themselves, their lives and the things they see around them. These stories help children to new understandings of events and actions. Through telling stories, children reflect, comment on and repackage their experience. They refocus and enlarge events so that the story evolves into a new experience, independent and able to outlast its original context.

When children create stories, they learn to use language to describe and sequence their ideas. Stories show the power of language to help people to understand themselves and to share their understandings and experiences with others.

Imaginative stories and young children

Children love stories. They love to read them, listen to them and watch them on television. Through play and conversations, they create and re-create stories about a myriad of things that have happened or could never happen.

Young children sometimes tell stories to entertain others, but mostly they do it because

inventing and telling stories is in itself pleasurable and emotionally satisfying.

A storyteller has complete control over the characters and the plot and is free to determine what happens. Through stories, children can explore different types of problems, provide explanations or explore alternative solutions. Like adults, young children use storytelling to understand real-life events and characters and to resolve unsatisfactory endings. However, whereas the adult is content to tell the story to a friend, often concluding with 'I wish I'd said...', children tend to re-create the story *with* a friend, enacting the characters and playing out the real and alternative endings as desired.

Creating stories through play

Children learn much about story-making through playing alone and with others. Play is useful because it is enjoyable and because it provides a forum for rehearsal: trying out ideas, experimenting with the different stories and the possible emphasis within a story. When children play together, they adopt the roles of both the storytellers and the listeners. Feedback from the audience is immediate. Exciting ideas are developed while others are dropped. As they choose to follow one story-line from the many possible, children learn about the infinite creativity of telling stories.

In play, children become the characters in their stories, adopting the appropriate body language, speech patterns and tone of voice. This helps young children to recognise that such differences between people exist and that they are an important part of characterisation. They may start with mimicry, copying characters and events from books, stories and people they know, but through play they re-form and change these characters, personalising them to create a rich bank of ideas for future stories.

This process of re-creation, generalisation and change is an important part of learning to tell stories. Talking with children about what happens in their stories, who the characters are, what distinguishes them, and what happens to move the story forward, helps the children to learn from each other, but, more importantly, it helps them to become conscious of what they know. In helping children to be explicit about this knowledge, teachers make it easier for children to draw on this when writing.

What children learn from reading

To want to write (rather than tell) their stories, young children need to know and believe that writing is powerful and that written stories are different from spoken ones. They need to recognise that writing can offer a permanent record so that a story can be told and retold in the absence of the teller. They also need to understand that writers must use different (and less immediate) techniques to convey posture, gestures or tone of voice; that writing takes longer than telling; and that writers, without the benefit of gesture, tone of voice or instant feedback in the form of audience reaction, must structure the events and choose their words carefully to convey the full story. Much of this knowledge is gained when children read stories.

Writing stories: what children need to learn

Writing stories down presents children with new challenges. The children are isolated when creating the story and are separated from the listener (Kress, 1982).

In play, children can think their way into a character or a situation by acting out the characters and events of the story. With the collaborative support of interested friends, they create new characters, choosing what they will do, how they move, what they say and how they speak. When the listeners are present and well-known, meanings can be conveyed with gestures, common understandings can be assumed and misunderstandings rapidly clarified.

This shared history and context does not exist when a story is to be written and read in the absence of the teller. Young children therefore have a doubly difficult task in writing: they must invent and imagine the story (often in the abstract, without friends, activity or actions to help), and they must also imagine the reader and the reader's reaction.

Project	Story type	Characterisation	Setting	Structure
The spider's shoes	Structure-driven story about imaginary context	Characterisation through dress and speech	Creating settings to suit characters, drawing detail in settings	A central problem drives the story
My favourite toy	Toy that comes to life	Using real toy to create character		Using a (magic) event to drive the story
The teddy bear who came to school	Magical story	Characterisation through appearance and preferences	Describing different places	
The magical travel machine	Fantasy adventure story	Thinking beyond stereotypes	Creating magical or fantasy settings	
Oh no, baby!	Structure-driven story about real-life context	Characterisation through action	Appropriate detail in settings	Using sequence for slow build-up of story; using place to structure the story
Zigzag robots	Imaginary character story	Characterisation through action, speech, dress and lifestyle		Using character to drive the story
This is me and this is what I'm like	Personal character story	Characterisation through action, lifestyle, speech and thoughts; character change over time		Repetition as a story device; using a set format to generate story
Holiday snaps	Personal experience story	Using real-people characterisation through feelings and speech	Using known settings; describing settings	Sequence; titles; an incident/problem creates a story
Our house is a very nice house, but one day...	Imaginary story about real-life context	Characterisation through action, speech and lifestyle	Using and describing known settings	A story needs one key incident to move it forward
No place like home	Imaginary character/setting mismatch	Characterisation through lifestyle	Creating settings to suit characters	Using lifestyle and setting to drive the story
Big box dens	Imaginative play story	All aspects; characters appropriate to setting	All aspects	Titles; front cover details
Meet my monster	Fantasy characters in real settings	Characterisation through action, speech and lifestyle	Using known settings	Stories need characters, setting and a problem

Scholastic
IMAGINATIVE WRITING
Workshop

Process	Collaborative demands	Approx. time-scale	Publication format/celebration
Using experience as readers to inform story characterisation	Low	One to two weeks	A4 book, shared with an important adult
Talk as a rehearsal strategy; using play to draft ideas	Low	One to three weeks	Four-page zigzag book; shared with important adult
Using real objects, play and talk to generate/rehearse the story	Low	One week	Teddy-shaped book; shared with peers
Possibilities with a story using play/collaboration to work through story possibilities	Medium to high	Two weeks	A4 book; shared with peers
Using stories to reflect on real life	Medium to high	Two weeks	A3 'big book' shared with peers
Creating and writing stories with a friend; using character to generate story	Medium to high	One week	A4 zigzag books; shared with peers
Writing and sharing stories with important adults; stories from real life	Low; higher level of collaboration with adult	Two to three weeks	A5 books; story shared with peers and important adult
Drafting/rehearsal through talk	Low	One week	A4-sized card book, reviewed by peers and one important adult
Writing from play/writing with a partner	Medium	One week	Zigzag book shared with peers
Writing with a partner	Medium	Two weeks	3D turning book; shared with peers
Using play as a strategy for generating/drafting stories	Low	One week	Card style book with lift up inner flap; shared with peers
	Low	Two weeks	A3 books with moveable monster; preview by older children

STORY PROJECTS

This volume contains:
- ideas and lesson plans for 12 writing projects;
- photocopiable activity sheets;
- ideas for publishing review and celebration of the children's work;
- ideas for further reading – books that children may be interested to read or discuss, either before or after a project;
- suggestions, advice and photocopiable pages for assessment and record-keeping.

The story projects

Each story project begins with a short overview providing a brief description of what the children do, a summary of its main focus, areas of support, its publication format and method of evaluation, celebration and review.

The projects offer a sequence of detailed lesson plans in which children generate ideas, write, publish and celebrate a story.

The projects enable the whole class to work on individual and collaborative stories. They cover a range of genres and topics and vary in length and focus. Teachers can select the project that best meets the needs and interests of the children in the time available. The content and focus of each project, including key areas of support, is summarised in the table on pages 8–9.

The importance of extended writing

The 'extended' nature of the projects allows children time to 'live' with a story for long enough to become emotionally involved with it and committed to writing it well. When children are given the space and time to think, feel and behave like writers, they discover their own recipes for success and begin to celebrate writing as both a process and a product.

The structure and sequence of the *Story Projects* activities ensure that each session acts as a springboard for the next. Play and practical activities provide a focus to help young writers generate new ideas and develop existing ones. They provide 'thinking time' and can change the pace of work, while maintaining the momentum of the story, allowing children to reflect on work done so far and to plan ahead. The projects encourage children to both work alone and with others and to discuss or 'play through' their stories at crucial points. For young children, this talk is often the 'first draft' of what their story will say.

Each project suggests original and exciting publishing formats, designed to entice both adults and children to read them. The experience of seeing others read and enjoy his or her work contributes to the young writer's sense of audience, ownership and self-esteem.

How do the projects relate to activities in *Crafting Stories*?

The story projects provide opportunities for learning about writing and the process of writing in an integrated, holistic way. They encourage children to think and behave like writers, to control their own stories, finding their own problems and solutions. In doing this, children will use many skills, techniques and strategies that are central to the writer's craft and they will learn about how writers think and behave and how they integrate, select, reflect and plan.

However, children also need a balance of learning experiences. A broad and balanced curriculum allows for holistic and focused learning experiences that target specific aspects of story writing in different ways. The activities in *Crafting Stories* complement the story projects. They allow teachers to be creative, flexible and analytical in their approach to teaching writing, choosing a story project or activities from *Crafting Stories* as required.

Developing reading–writing links

The stories that children find easy to write relate to the type of stories that they experience as readers, and this will vary within a class. Teachers need to provide good examples of different types of writing for children to read, share and discuss. For this reason, each project is accompanied by a list of books which can be used to provide ideas or models for particular projects.

CLASSROOM MANAGEMENT

Involving the whole class

Inspiration and creativity are infectious and the projects are most effective when they involve the whole class, rather than one or two groups. Projects with the whole class mean that the children benefit from seeing and responding to a wider range of ideas than can be generated within a single group. They provide an opportunity for children to work with a wider range of partners. For teachers, they simplify time-consuming aspects of forward planning and collecting and organising resources, freeing them to focus on the task of observing, teaching and working alongside the children.

Planning time for the projects

To allow the ideas to develop continuity and momentum, the story projects should be treated as concentrated 'blocks' of work. When too much time elapses between writing sessions, the children lose enthusiasm; they forget where they have to go to, lose the momentum of the previous session and the end-product is a long time coming. Flexible timetabling that allows children three to five sessions per week for a project is ideal. Curricular areas that miss out during the project can be given additional time before and after it. It is worth the reorganisation: one, concentrated project in which children are eager to write is a more effective and enjoyable learning situation than several shorter activities in which unwilling children are cajoled and pushed into producing something on paper.

Organising the class

Many of the projects involve children working with others and it is important that they keep to the same partner or group for all the sessions within a project. It is best if children work with a friend, or someone they feel comfortable with, although obviously the teacher must retain the right to veto some pairings!

Children should work with different writing partners or groups for each new project, since this ensures that they work with a range of people in the class and benefit from different working relationships and the different viewpoints, feedback and advice they generate.

Choosing and organising resources for publication

It is important that children have good quality materials if they are to take a pride in the presentation of their work. For most projects, children will need:
• good quality paper on which to write or mount their writing;
• colouring pens (both thick and thin felt-tipped pens) and coloured pencils for illustrations;
• a variety of shapes and sizes of paper suitable for writing and for illustrations;
• collage materials to inspire the children – for example, small quantities of sequins, netting, gold and silver foil, shiny paper, fabrics, wrapping paper, and Christmas decorations which have been cut up into small pieces;
• scissors, PVA glue and spreaders.

Each table of children can be given their own project tray containing all the materials they need.

The project activities

The following information is given by symbols at the beginning of each activity:
Class organisation details whether the children will be working individually, or in pairs, in larger groups, or as a class.
Time required gives an idea of how long each activity may take. Obviously, this can only be a rough estimate and will be governed by individual teachers and classes.

Each activity is structured under the following headings:
Teaching content explains the main teaching objectives of each activity.
What you need details at a glance the resources required for the session.
What to do explains exactly how to introduce and structure each lesson.
Pre-session provides ideas which may be used as an introduction to a project. This brief section occurs in those projects for which it is appropriate.

Using the story books

Some of the children's books included in this *Scholastic Writing Workshop* can be used in conjunction with the writing projects to inspire ideas and provide good examples of genre.

Bibliography

Calkins, Lucy McKormick (1986) *The Art of Teaching Writing*, Heinemann
Kress, G. (1982) *Learning to Write*, Routledge.

Chapter Two

ASSESSMENT

ASSESSMENT

The story projects allow teachers to observe and work with children on their writing over a period of time. This allows them to form a picture of each child that is informed by a rich variety of evidence: from talk; from play; from drawing; and from writing. Teachers assess all the time and cannot help but notice and take account of:

• what children do;
• what children say about what they have done;
• what children find easy or difficult, or can do only with help;
• what type of help is most useful;
• what gives the children particular pleasure or enjoyment;
• what the children do not like and why;
• the work the children produce.

It is important that assessment and record-keeping should support rather than divert teachers from analysing needs and providing appropriate teaching input and learning activities. It is, after all, this match that determines the progress children make.

General assessment and record-keeping photocopiable pages

The assessment and record-keeping pages in this book are intended to link with and complement those in the *Crafting Stories* volume. Teachers should only use those that they find helpful.

Class/group project notes (page 16) – formative assessment

The class/group project notes are intended to provide an informal record of particular children who stood out during the project and a record of why they did so. Teachers may use them throughout the project, on a daily basis if necessary. They are divided into two broad sections: 'The project in class' and 'Writing craft development'. These are obviously not exclusive, but the division may help teachers to analyse where the general needs and strengths of the class lie. As teachers add comments to the class record over the course of a story project, they will find that some names crop up frequently and others less frequently, if at all. It is often productive to consider why some children are not mentioned, if only so that the teacher can be sure that it is because their needs are being met rather than because they are being overlooked.

Individual project report (page 17) – formative/summative assessment

The individual project report is intended to help teachers analyse children's work with a view to identifying achievement, appropriate support or challenges in future. It targets three important areas:

• *The child as a writer*. This includes information on what the child enjoyed or disliked, found easy or hard. It allows the teacher to comment on observations about the child's preferred strategies for rehearsal, planning, and writing, as well as on the child's attitudes (the immediacy of the story to the child; commitment and involvement in it; motivation to tell it well; sense of voice; purpose and audience) during the project and once the story has been published and read.
• *Teacher comment on the story written*. This allows the teacher to use the 'crafting stories' framework to analyse how the child has chosen to tell the story – commenting on the strongest aspects of characterisation, setting or structure, and on the nature and range of the writing strategies used.
• *Teacher–child discussion*. This allows the teacher to record and comment on the child's evaluation in the light of the teacher's observations. It assumes that teachers have discussed the story project with the child.

Teachers must choose when to do an individual project report, and should not necessarily feel the need to do one for every child on each writing project, although they

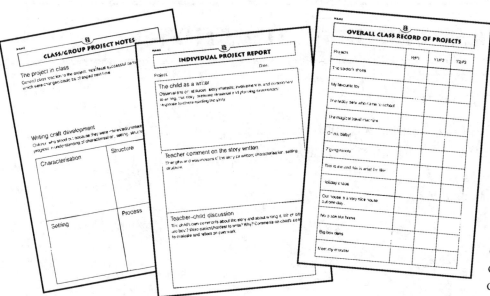

• children often recognise strengths and weaknesses in another's story before they can do so in their own;

• children have to justify their opinions, which encourages them to be analytical and promotes deep learning – through articulating and explaining ideas, children broaden, clarify and consolidate their understanding;

• young children often respond to stories that have been written by someone they know in a different way from those written by professional authors. This encourages reading–writing links – they use their experience as readers to help them write.

should plan to assess all children over a period of time.

Overall record of story projects (page 18)

This is a record of the story projects covered each year and can be passed on to subsequent teachers of the class.

Providing feedback for the child

None of the assessment formats is intended to provide specific comments or feedback for the child on how the story could be improved. In part, this is because the end of a project is too late for such advice, which is most helpful during the writing process while the children are making decisions and crafting the story. The assessment formats alert the teacher to the kinds of advice and support the children may need in future.

Once the projects have been published, the teacher's feedback to the children needs to celebrate their achievements and encourage them to share in the achievements of others.

Self-evaluation and peer evaluation

Self-evaluation and peer evaluation is integral to each story project and to many of the activities in *Crafting Stories*. Self-evaluation is important because it helps children to become efficient and effective learners.

• It helps to make children aware of what they know and what they can do.

• It provides a basis from which to analyse learning, needs, monitor progress and to celebrate good work.

• It develops self-knowledge, confidence and self-esteem.

Peer evaluation provides an equally powerful tool for learning. It is important because:

Summative assessment

It is recommended that teachers keep a portfolio of the work of each child. This might contain:

• stories from the story projects;

• writing produced in response to the *Crafting Stories* activities;

• evaluations and comments by the child;

• observations, evaluations and comments by the teacher, other readers, or people with whom the child worked;

• writing review forms (see *Crafting Stories*, page 18) completed by the child and/or the teacher.

Teachers need to devise their own policy for what is included in the writer's portfolio. There are several options:

• predetermine specific pieces of work to be included in all portfolios;

• determine set 'portfolio review times' when either the teacher or the children review the contents and balance of each portfolio, adding work as appropriate;

• encourage children to consider adding work to the portfolios as it is completed.

Teachers will find that over a period of time they have built up a detailed profile of each child as a writer. A review of the child's portfolio and of the teacher's formative assessment notes will provide ample evidence on which summative and evaluative reports can be written.

CLASS/GROUP PROJECT NOTES

The project in class

General class reaction to the project, most/least successful parts; aspects which were changed/could be changed next time.

Writing craft development

Children who stood out because they were interested/uninterested; made progress in understanding of characterisation, setting, structure or process.

Characterisation	Structure
Setting	Process

INDIVIDUAL PROJECT REPORT

Project: Date:

The child as a writer

Observations on: attitudes; story interests; involvement in, and commitment to writing, this story; preferred rehearsal and planning experiences; response to others reading the story.

Teacher comment on the story written

Strengths and weaknesses of the story as written; characterisation, setting, structure.

Teacher–child discussion

The child's own comments about the story and about writing it. Which bits are best? Were easiest/hardest to write? Why? Comments on child's ability to evaluate and reflect on own work.

OVERALL CLASS RECORD OF PROJECTS

Projects	R/P1	Y1/P2	Y2/P3
The spider's shoes			
My favourite toy			
The teddy bear who came to school			
The magical travel machine			
Oh no, baby!			
Zigzag robots			
This is me and this is what I'm like			
Holiday snaps			
Our house is a very nice house, but one day...			
No place like home			
Big box dens			
Meet my monster			

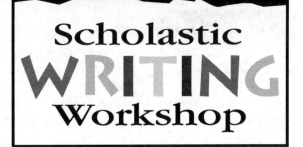

Chapter Three

THE SPIDER'S SHOES

INTRODUCTION

Project description

In this project the children make an A4 book about a spider who needs four pairs of shoes to go to a party. In writing the story, the children have to consider carefully how the different characters speak, and create a setting that is appropriate for each one. Before this project, in the first activity, the children make, and play with, a collection of toy spiders, or listen to several stories which feature minibeasts and include strong characterisations. This encourages them to think about a range of insects and spiders which have distinct personalities and prepares them for the discussion of different aspects of the characters who are featured in this project.

The project begins when the children make their own spider and invent its character. Each spider receives an invitation to a party. The invitation, from Tallulah Tippytoes, explains that, because there will be plenty of dancing, she is sending the spider a beautiful pair of shoes. But Tallulah has forgotten that spiders have eight legs and the poor spider needs to borrow another three pairs of shoes to wear.

Over the course of the next three sessions, the children select two characters from a selection of characters presented on two photocopiable sheets, who will each lend the spider one pair of shoes. The characters are very different from one another and each character must be placed in a suitable setting and given appropriate shoes. The children complete speech bubbles (and optional thought bubbles) to show how their spider speaks to each character and how the characters respond. The final pair of shoes is borrowed from a real-life character whom the children know well.

On the final page, the children draw the spider at the party, with a selection of other characters, all of them in party dress. One character in this scene is a special person: it is a picture of the adult who will be asked to enjoy the book with the child and to complete the celebration/evaluation sheet.

Then the children choose a title and design a front cover for their book. If appropriate, they are given the opportunity to review their story and add a narrative story-line before sharing it with their specified adult.

Why this context?

Children will be familiar with, and excited by, the format of this book. The project offers choice within a clear structure and does not make too many writing demands on the children.

In addition to this context giving children an opportunity to invent a character, they have to consider how different characters speak and how they relate to each other. The context uses drawing to emphasise the importance of detail in describing settings that are appropriate for different characters. It also offers an opportunity for children to discuss and understand how a narrative commentary can help to make stories unambiguous to new readers.

Project organisation

This project involves minimal collaboration. The children work individually to make their spider characters and write their stories. Support is given by the strong story structure and through whole-class discussion and discussion between the teacher and individual children.

Publication, celebration and review

In this project children make an A4-sized story book, consisting of six landscape sheets, stapled together. The main character, a spider, is made as a separate collage and is attached to the book by means of a thread tied through a hole made in the top left-hand corner of the cover. This allows the spider to be placed in the middle of any scene, drawn on any page, in the book.

The adult who is chosen by the child, and features as a character at the end of the book, is asked to complete an appreciation sheet which is fixed, as a book review, to the back cover of the book.

Books the children may find useful

How Many Bugs in a Box?, David A. Carter (1989) Orchard Books
The Bad-Tempered Ladybird, Eric Carle (1982) Puffin
Spider! Hedgehog Hunt, Graham Ralph and John Cary (1993) BBC Children's Books
Spider! Little Miss M, Graham Ralph and John Cary (1993) BBC Children's Books
Omnibombulator, Dick King-Smith (1995) Doubleday
The Enchanted Wood, Gerald Hawksley (1991) Treehouse Children's Books
The Jolly Postman, Janet and Allan Ahlberg (1986) Heinemann
On the Way Home, Jill Murphy (1984) Macmillan

SPIDERS

Teaching content
Spiders may have different characters.

What you need
Spider toys collected by the children or a selection of books; labels.

What to do
Preparation for this project can begin several weeks before you introduce the idea of the children inventing and writing stories of their own. This activity provides an ideal introduction to the project by encouraging the children to talk about and play with a class collection of toy spiders. Ensure that you include a fair number of friendly, cuddly spiders, as well as the more predictable, plastic spiders which children may find more frightening.

Make some labels to place in front of the collection, which highlight possible characteristics (for example, Can you find a grumpy/friendly/proud/shy spider? Which spider likes to run/play/read/sleep?).

Alternatively, you may like to read a selection of stories about minibeasts. This should be done several weeks before the children start writing their own stories, or you will find that they may reproduce these story-lines in their own work. (See the list of books on the opposite page.)

MEET MY SPIDER

Teaching content
Inventing a character.

What you need
A4 blank story book made up for each child with six sheets (12 pages) stapled together on the short side and with a front and back cover made of card. Craft materials, hole punch, string or wool, scissors, glue, sticky tape, coloured sugar paper, writing materials.

What to do
Once the children have spent time thinking about spiders – the range of their appearance, personalities and habits – it is time for them to start inventing their own spider character and writing about it.

Give the children a range of craft materials, coloured sugar paper, scissors, glue and sticky tape. Show them the materials and tell them that you would like them to make a spider of their very own. They must decide what sort of spider to make. They should choose the most appropriate size and shape (within specific limits – no spider should be larger than the book they will be making) and select the best colours and textures to use. Explain that every spider in the class will be different – in name, appearance and personality.

While the children are making their spider ask them to decide on:
• its name;
• who their spider would admire, who it would regard with disdain and what it would say and do if it met these people;
• what their spider likes to do for fun.

While the children are working, talk to them about their spiders and the reasons for their choice of colours, materials and so on. Encourage them to talk freely about their spider's personality and how this is evidenced by its appearance.

When the children have finished, help them to attach a length of string to their spider. The string should be long enough to enable it to be tied to the top left-hand corner of the front cover but still allow the spider to 'visit' each page.

Tell the children that they are going to write a story about their spider and give them the books that have been made up. Show them how to use the hole punch to make a hole in the top left-hand corner of the cover and help them to tie their spider on to this. Write each child's name *lightly* on the cover of their book in pencil.

Once the spiders have been made, put the children into pairs and ask them to tell each other about their spiders. Then ask them to write a short description of their spider's character. They may find the following writing frame useful for this:
Meet .... (spider's name)
He/she is interesting because ....
He/she likes to ....

This writing will form the introduction to the story and can be pasted or written on page 1 of each child's story book.

3
THE PARTY INVITATION
✝ (20)

Teaching content
Characterisation through inner speech, and the use of thought bubbles.

What you need
Option 1 – photocopiable page 27. Option 2 – selection of shop-bought party invitations, writing and drawing materials. For the rest of the activity – envelopes, catalogues (for pictures of shoes), scissors, glue, photocopiable pages 28 to 30, writing and drawing materials.

What to do
This session has two possible options to ensure that each spider gets a party invitation. Option 1 involves simply giving the spider a party invitation. It encourages the story to gather pace quickly and has a good surprise element. Option 2 involves children making party invitations for each other. It offers teaching opportunities for functional writing and the chance for children to read each other's work. Because their own work will feature in another child's story, children will be keen to read these stories and to share them with parents and friends.

However, making the invitations will take a complete session on its own and for some children it may interrupt, and therefore detract from, the story-line. Choose whichever option is most appropriate for the class.

Option 1: Complete the invitation on photocopiable page 27, one for each child's spider. Put the invitations into envelopes and hide the envelopes in a place where the children are sure to find them: in their trays, PE bags, a big box or parcel that arrives in the classroom, in the story corner or the play house and so on.

Option 2: Show the children the collection of party invitation cards. Compile a class list of the essential information on them. Ask the children to each make a party invitation, giving them the name of another child's spider to whom it is to be sent. Ensure that each spider receives an invitation.

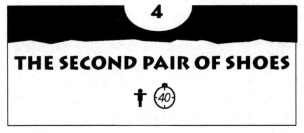

THE SECOND PAIR OF SHOES
✝ 🕐40

Once the invitations have been received, they should be pasted, with their envelopes, on to page 2 of the book.

When the children have read their spider's invitations, allow them to look through the catalogues and cut out the pair of shoes that their spider has been sent. Using photocopiable page 28, ask each child to complete a 'thought bubble' showing the spider's thoughts – what it said to itself about the party invitation and what it thought about its new shoes. This can then be stuck on to page 3, leaving enough space for the spider on the string to be dangled on the page, with the thought bubble arising from its head.

Explain to the children that there is only one problem that could prevent their spider from going to the party... it needs more than one pair of shoes, but has no money to buy some. Help the children to count how many feet the spider has and to work out how many more pairs of shoes it will need. Ask the children to suggest solutions to the problem.

The children may suggest that their spider borrow some shoes. If they do not suggest this, put it to them as a solution to the spider's problem. Show the class an enlarged copy of photocopiable pages 29 and 30. Tell them that their spider might visit some of these people to borrow shoes. Ask them to each choose one person their spider would like to visit. Explain that in the next lesson, they will write about this visit.

Teaching content
Characterisation through choice of clothes (shoes) and environment. Different characters speak differently and this may depend on to whom they are talking.

What you need
Photocopiable pages 29, 30 and 31, photocopiable page 28 (optional), chalkboard, scissors, glue, writing and drawing materials.

What to do
Write the sentence 'Oh no! I need more shoes to wear' on the board. Ask the children to copy this across the bottom of page 3 of their books, or give them a written strip with these words on it to glue into place.

Show the class the enlarged copies of photocopiable pages 29 and 30 which you used in the previous session, showing the pictures of different characters. Point out that we can't see the shoes of any of these characters, and explain that the children will have to imagine what the shoes will be like.

Tell the children to pick one character from whom their spider will borrow a pair of shoes. They could either draw their own version of this character, or colour and cut out a character from an A4 copy of photocopiable pages 29 and 30. While they draw or colour, tell the children to think about where their particular character would live and what their home might look like inside. Encourage them to discuss this as they work. The character should be drawn or stuck on to the right-hand page of the double-page spread (page 5 of the child's book), preferably somewhere towards the centre fold, leaving the facing page (page 4) blank.

Then ask the children to draw an appropriate background for the character – perhaps a spell room for the wizard, a palace for the queen or a caravan for the clown. Tell the children that the character's shoes should be visible somewhere in this room, or on the blank facing page.

Children who are young, or new to making books, should be encouraged just to draw appropriate shoes for the character. However, an older class which copes easily with this type of activity could incorporate the shoes under a 'lift the flap' mechanism as a surprise. Alternatively, they could draw the shoes on separate pieces of paper and then paste them on to the picture, or store them in a specially made pocket. This enables the spider to take the shoes away physically, but you do run the risk of losing (and forever hunting for) individual shoes that are missing somewhere in the classroom!

Finally, give out copies of photocopiable page 31 and ask the children to think how their spider would go about asking to borrow a pair of shoes from this character. Would the spider be polite or demanding, obsequious or proud? Would it stutter in embarrassment or put forward an eloquent argument about why it deserves to use the shoes? Children should write this in the top speech bubble. They should think about how their cut-out character would speak and write a suitable positive reply in the second speech bubble. These should be cut out and glued on to page 4 of their book. If the children wish, they can also add 'thought bubbles' (from a copy of photocopiable page 28) to show what either, or both, characters are thinking.

It is not necessary for children to redraw their spider, since the 'real' one can be put in, on its string, when each page is read.

End the activity by showing the children the enlarged photocopies of the characters again. Tell them that their spider now has two pairs of shoes. Help them to work out how many more pairs it has to borrow. Explain that tomorrow it will visit someone else to borrow another pair of shoes.

THE THIRD PAIR OF SHOES

Teaching content
Characterisation through speech, dress and environment.

What you need
Photocopiable pages 29, 30 and 31, photocopiable page 28 (optional), scissors, glue, writing and drawing materials.

What to do
Remind the children of what has happened so far by asking them to draw the two pairs of shoes their spider has already borrowed at the bottom of page 6. Then run this session in exactly the same way as the previous session.

End the activity by telling the children that their spider must borrow the final pair of shoes from a real person – someone the children know in real life – it might be a parent or grandparent, a friend, a favourite neighbour, a teacher, or another adult they know. Suggest that they think about this and bring a firm idea of who it will be and of the shoes they wear to the next session.

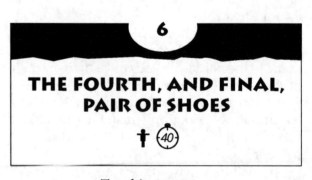

THE FOURTH, AND FINAL, PAIR OF SHOES

Teaching content
Using real-life characters, dress and environment.

What you need
Photocopiable page 31, photocopiable page 28 (optional), writing and drawing materials, catalogues which have pictures of shoes (optional).

What to do

Run this session in the same way as the previous sessions, asking the children to draw someone they know as their chosen character in appropriate surroundings and to complete the speech bubbles (and/or thought bubbles). The children can either use the catalogues to cut out appropriate shoes for the person they have drawn or they can draw the shoes they think this person would wear.

End by telling the children that tomorrow they will complete the final page of their story – the party scene.

peeping out from under cloaks/dresses. Their spider should be drawn in pride of place, wearing all its finery and four beautiful pairs of shoes!

8

MAKING THE COVER

†　40

Teaching content
Function and information on front cover. Choosing a title.

What you need
A selection of books (chosen for the different styles and layouts of their front covers), craft and collage materials, chalkboard, computer (if required), writing and drawing materials.

What to do
Show the children the books you have selected. Establish that all covers have a title and the name of the author written on them. Point out to the children that different typefaces and styles are used for the writing. Mention that usually the cover of a book is bright and eye-catching, and has appropriate drawings which tell you something about the story or the characters.

Talk to the children briefly about a title for their own book. You may want to generate a long list of suggestions and write these on the board.

Give out the drawing and collage materials. Tell the children that you would like them to choose a title for their story and to decide where and how to write the title on the front cover. They will also need to think about where they would like their own name to be written on the front cover. Explain how lettering of the title and the author may be produced. You could demonstrate this at a computer, or have a range of possible titles and suitable layouts already prepared for the children to use. The

7

THE PARTY AT LAST!

†　40

Teaching content
Story endings resolve the central problem of the story.

What you need
Photocopiable pages 29 and 30, drawing materials.

What to do
Tell the children that in this lesson they will be drawing the party scene where their spider will be able to wear all its new shoes.

Let the children look at photocopiable pages 29 and 30 again and decide who they would like to invite to the party. Remind the children about the party background details they may wish to draw: bunting, party streamers, decorations, balloons, party food and so on. The children may choose to draw characters who have already featured in their story, or entirely new characters. They may like to combine coloured-in characters from the photocopiable sheets with their own drawings of people they know.

Explain that the children will be reading their story to one adult they know well. They should draw this person at the party, as a surprise for the reader. Remind the children to think about the clothes and colours that would be worn for a party and to add any additional details such as hairbands, crowns, jewellery and shoes children may wish to write their own title and devise an appropriate layout themselves.

Finally, ask the children to finish the front cover for their story by decorating it carefully or drawing and colouring their design.

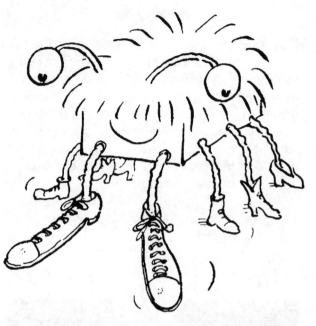

9

ADDING A NARRATIVE SCRIPT

†/††/†††† ○

Teaching content
Narrative writing.

What you need
Writing materials.

What to do
You may wish some, or all, of the children to write a narrative for the books they have made. Through rereading their own books and reading the books of others, children often realise that adding a narrative makes a story easier to follow. A narrative can be written for the book simply by writing a short explanatory statement at the top or bottom of each page, or double-page spread.

Some children may like to do this alone. Others may prefer to work in pairs, or in small groups with the teacher. It may be possible to use children from an older class as appreciative listeners who could help children decide on what, if anything, they would like to add to their stories. Of course if this latter option is chosen, the older children need to be carefully briefed. It is important that they understand the supportive nature of their role and appreciate the importance of giving clear, positive feedback and support.

10

CELEBRATION AND REVIEW

† ○

Teaching content
Celebration of writing and stories.

What you need
Photocopiable page 32.

What to do
Give the children an opportunity to share their books and to practise reading them to other children in the class.

Ask the children to name the real-life adult who is illustrated in their final party scene. It will be someone who is important to them and who they think would enjoy the book. Read and explain the contents of photocopiable page 32, and tell the children that it should be completed by this person.

The children can either take the book home, along with a copy of photocopiable page 32 for the adult to complete, or the school can invite all the adults to a class book launch or book afternoon. Once completed, the lower half of the photocopiable sheets can be stapled to the back of the book as a book review. It is important that the children are encouraged to bring the books and completed photocopiable sheets back to school to share with their classmates.

INVITATION TO THE PARTY

Dear

Please come to my party

on

at

We will have such fun. All our friends will be there!

with love from
Tallulah Tippytoes

PS There is going to be LOTS of dancing. I'm
sending you a beautiful pair of party shoes to wear.

WHAT I THINK...

Scholastic
IMAGINATIVE WRITING
Workshop

CHOOSE SOME SHOES

CHOOSE SOME SHOES

Scholastic
IMAGINATIVE WRITING
Workshop

WHAT I WOULD SAY...

CELEBRATION AND REVIEW

Name of author _____

Dear adult,

To make the best progress in writing, children need to share their stories with people who are important to them. Our class have recently been writing story books about spiders.

This young author has chosen you to be the first person to hear this story. You are very privileged! Please make time to read the story carefully and talk about it with the child. It would be very helpful if you could write brief answers to the questions below and explain what you have written to the child.

Many thanks.

◆   What do you like most about this book?

◆   From talking to the author, what do you think he/she likes most about the book?

◆   Look carefully at the last page. Do you recognise anyone at the party? If not, please ask the author to point out the surprise guest.

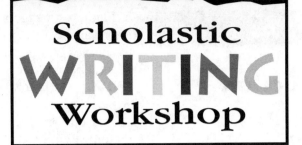

WRITING

Workshop

Chapter Four

MY FAVOURITE TOY

INTRODUCTION

Project description

In the first activity of this project the children state what their favourite toy is, writing this down on a photocopiable sheet, and then drawing three things about the toy – what it looks like, how they play with it and where they play with it – and then writing why it is a favourite toy. This forms the cover of an individual book. The children are then introduced to a plain cardboard box and asked what they could do to make it look like a toy-box. The children decorate the box and go on to complete a photocopiable sheet of a toy-box for their book.

The story-line continues with a session where a 'magic wand' is waved over the toy-box, changing the toys within it, but in what way? The children are asked to predict and imagine through role-play. Finally, the children complete their individual 'toy' book using structured text – 'I put it in the toy-box, waved a magic wand and look what happened next' – to predict an ending for the story.

Why this context?

This project offers children ownership of a story which is about their own toy. The imaginative play situation of a magic toy-box within the classroom is used to develop the children's story-making skills, and this is built upon to enhance the written format.

The context offers opportunities to develop children's imaginations and takes them from the reality of a situation – their own toy – to the prediction of their own endings through the magic of the toy-box. There are many other ideas within the book to develop ideas on the magic theme.

The context is one which may be carried out in a short period of time or may last as long as the children are involved through imaginative play with the toy-box.

Project organisation

This context offers opportunities for children to work within a variety of groupings. At the start of the context small groups of four draw upon previous experience and share ideas about their favourite toys, before beginning their individual zigzag books. Class discussion is important at given points throughout the context to enable children to talk about the front covers of their books, decide upon descriptive words, and in feedback sessions to share play experience with the toy-box. Children can collaborate in the directed tasks of selecting materials with which to decorate the big box.

The project involves specific thought for the teacher about the position of the big box in the classroom. It may help to set it up in an area which will provide sufficient space for children to be actively involved in role-play and movement.

The final part of the context will enable all children to share their stories with a friend and evaluate the variety of endings.

Publication, celebration and review

In this context, children make a story book consisting of four pages fastened together with sticky tape to make a zigzag book on to which the photocopiable sheets are pasted. Inside, within a pocket, children make their own miniature magic wand to wave over the toy-box, before the resolution on the last page. The toy-box on the second photocopiable sheet should be cut to enable the lid to open and a picture of the toy to be stuck inside. The picture could be photocopied from the cover or children could be asked to draw one which is similar. The resolution to the story is presented on the last page.

Once completed, the books are placed in the book corner of the classroom for informal sharing and celebration. After a few days, the children are given a more formal opportunity to read and share their story with a friend. On this occasion, the children are asked to help each other to complete a photocopiable sheet. The first half is completed by the author who notes down which aspects of the writing and reading he or she most enjoyed. The second half is completed by the friend, who is asked to draw the part of the story that he or she liked best.

Books the children may find useful

The Magic Suit, Roger Smith (1991) Macmillan Children's Books
All the Magic in the World, Wendy Hartman, illustrated by Nick Daly (1993) Bodley Head

1
MY FAVOURITE TOY
卌-卌 ○

Teaching content

Characteristics of the toy, action and setting within the child's everyday situations.

What you need

Children's own toys, photocopiable page 39, pre-cut sugar paper – slightly larger than A4 size, egg-timer/bell (optional), writing and drawing materials.

What to do

Before beginning the project, it would be helpful to read stories which involve 'magic' creating change in characteristics or objects, for example *The Magic Suit* by Roger Smith and *All the Magic in the World* by Wendy Hartmann.

Prior to the session, ask the children to bring a favourite small toy to school, with their parents' permission. They should think about why they like it more than others, what it looks like, what they do with it and where they play with it. Parental involvement will be necessary to ensure that nothing too large, valuable or breakable is brought to school. Begin by organising the children into small groups of four and tell them that each child will be allowed two minutes to talk about his or her toy and the questions they had to think about before the session. You may use an egg-timer or bell to signify the two minutes – the emphasis here is to allow each child to participate.

When all of the children have taken a turn to speak, give out copies of photocopiable page 39. Ask them to draw and write some of the ideas they have just discussed using the photocopiable sheet. Explain which boxes will require drawing and in which boxes they will write (the first and last boxes) – you may have to scribe for some children.

Encourage the children to take their time with this as it will form the front cover of their book. As the children finish working, go round the groups and stick the front cover on to a slightly larger piece of pre-cut sugar paper.

Finally, bring the children together as a class and ask for volunteers to talk about the front cover of their book. The children should take their toys home at the end of the session.

2
MAKING A TOY-BOX
Ⓦ-卌 ○

Teaching content

Building a description of the class toy-box.

What you need

One large cardboard box, craft materials, magazines containing pictures of toys, wrapping paper which has pictures of toys, felt-tipped pens, paint or glossy paper, two large sheets of paper.

What to do

Gather the whole class together and show the children the large cardboard box. Tell them that they are going to change this into a really attractive toy-box. Let the children offer suggestions about the colour, materials, pictures and so on that they would like to use to decorate the box and show them the range of resources that you have gathered. Using a large piece of paper, record all of the items that the children will use to cover the box.

If the box requires painting, select a small group of two to three children to do this. Ask the other children to work in small groups and allocate specific cutting and selecting tasks. This will be a very active session! It may be helpful to use a recording sheet to allocate these tasks. For example:

We will use:
• pictures from magazines;
• choose sequins;
• children's names;
• cut-out toys from fablon.

Each group in turn should be asked to decorate the box with the resources they have selected until all of the children have contributed and the box has been decorated.

Bring the whole class together again, with the toy-box as a focal point, and ask the children to think of words that could describe their box. For example, the children may suggest 'bright', 'colourful', 'full of toys' and so on. Record these words on a large piece of paper and use them at a later date to make labels to locate near the box, either on the wall or even on the box itself.

For the next session, ask the children to think about what they will put on their own picture of a toy-box.

3

MY TOY-BOX

Teaching content

Creating an individual front cover for each child's book.

What you need

Photocopiable page 40, craft material (sequins, stars), pictures of toys cut out of magazines, stickers, scissors, glue, sticky tape.

What to do

This session follows on from the class activity carried out in the previous session except that, in this case, children are designing a two-dimensional box on photocopiable page 40 and covering it in appropriate materials.

Give each child a copy of photocopiable page 40, and a selection of resources from which they may choose. Tell the children that they may also select any of the pictures at the foot of the photocopiable sheet to cut, stick on to their toy-box, and then colour.

When they have decorated their page, the children should write four words in the boxes provided which best describes their toy-box. As in Session 1, this photocopiable sheet should be stuck on to sugar paper and secured with sticky tape to form page 2 of their zigzag book.

4

USING THE TOY-BOX

Teaching content
Story-making through imaginative play.

What you need
Toys from within the classroom, LEGO, large 'toy-box' created in Session 2, area for imaginative play, magic wand, musical instruments (optional).

What to do
Gather the children together and remind them of the toy-box that they made. Explain that in this activity they have to imagine that this is not just an ordinary toy-box, but a box that does magic when a wand is waved over it.

Show the children the magic wand you have brought in. Ask a child to bring you a toy from the classroom, for example some pieces of LEGO, and put it in the box. Ask the children to think of stories they have read about magic – what do you do with the wand? Are there special words to say? 'Perform' some magic and ask the children to predict what might happen to the pieces of LEGO. Children may suggest that the LEGO goes flying around, sticks to the sides of the box, builds itself into a house and so on.

Explain to the children that the magic only happens inside the box and that they will not see it happen – they just have to *imagine*. You will also have to explain that when the magic is finished and they open the box, the object inside will be exactly the same as when it was originally put in. The 'timing' of the magic may be dependent on:
• the magic words said or the spell performed;
• children closing their eyes and counting to ten;
• your reading of a magic poem;
• the use of a sand timer.

The emphasis in this part of the session should be on discussion with the children about what they have imagined happening to the LEGO inside the box.

This part of the session should act as a stimulus for the children's play with the box and the toys. Set it up in an area where there is some space for movement – the children may act out what they think is happening in the box. The playing of musical instruments could be added for effect.

Throughout this period of play, which may be carried out over several sessions to enable every child to participate, your role involves observation, interaction with the children to develop their story-making skills, perhaps adding appropriate resources, and certainly, in feedback sessions, encouraging the children to tell their 'stories' to the others.

5

THE MAGIC WAND

Teaching content
Devising an ending to a story

What you need
Photocopiable page 41, straw or lollipop sticks, star shapes, glitter, glue, sequins, coloured square for pockets, paper, sugar paper.

What to do
Before beginning this session, ask the children to close their eyes and think again about their favourite toy. Tell them to think what might happen if they put their toy into the magic box and were able to see inside as the magic was

Scholastic
IMAGINATIVE WRITING
Workshop

working. Tell them that in this session they will be making their own magic wand. Tell the children to keep thinking as they decorate their magic wand. Hand out the appropriate materials and let the children decorate their wand with glitter, sequins and so on. The wand should be about A3 size.

Give each child a copy of photocopiable page 41 and ask the children to design and colour in a pocket for the sheet in which they can keep their wand. They may need help to paste this on to the photocopiable page to ensure easy access of the wand. This forms the third page of their zigzag book and should be stuck on to sugar paper as before.

The final part of this session requires the children to draw what happened next. Before doing this they should draw a small picture of their favourite toy, big enough to fit into the lid of the box on page 2 of the zigzag books when opened. Using their book, they should now enact their story saying the words on photocopiable page 41: 'I put it in the toy-box, waved a magic wand', at which point they should cut out this small picture and attach it to the lid of their box. They should then take their own magic wand, wave it over the box and on a piece of paper they should draw what happened next. At the top of the page tell the children to write 'and look what happened next'. You may or may not wish them to write about it. The essential feature of this context is that there will be many different endings. Paste this sheet on to sugar paper to create page four and the end of the zigzag book.

SHARING THE STORY WITH A FRIEND

Teaching content
Publication, celebration and review.

What you need
Books the children have written, photocopiable page 42.

What to do
Once the stories have been written, make a display of them in the book corner in the classroom. Make a point of talking to the children about the stories written by their classmates and encourage them to read them with you and with each other.

After a few days, it is a good idea to provide the children with a more formal opportunity to share their stories. Ask the children to each collect their book and to choose a friend to work with. Explain that you want the children to read and talk about their story with their friend. State that you would be interested to know what the children most liked about writing and then reading their stories aloud, and what they most enjoyed about each other's story.

Give each child a copy of photocopiable page 42 and read it through with the class. Show the children how to fill in the details in the first box. Suggest that one child in each pair begins by reading his or her story. Immediately after reading it, he or she should try to answer the questions in the second box, helped by the child who listened to the story. Finally, the child who listened should respond to the story by completing the final two sections of the photocopiable sheet, helped if necessary by the author of the story.

The children should then swap roles and again help each other to complete the appropriate sections of the photocopiable sheet. When the photocopiable sheets have been completed, they should be displayed in the book corner, if possible, beside the story books to which they refer.

MY FAVOURITE TOY

My favourite toy is

This is what it looks like.

This is what I do with it.

This is where I play with it.

It is my favourite toy because

MY TOY-BOX

THE MAGIC WAND

I put it in the toy box,

waved

a

m a g i c

wand

SHARING THE STORY WITH A FRIEND

Name _

My story is called _

I read my story to my friend _

When I read this story aloud, I like

The best bit about making and writing this story was

What I like about 'magic' stories is

I listened to the story. I thought the story was (please tick):

good fun   scary   funny   exciting   wonderful

Draw the part of the story you liked most.

Scholastic
IMAGINATIVE WRITING
Workshop

Chapter Five

THE TEDDY
BEAR WHO CAME
TO SCHOOL

INTRODUCTION

Project description

In this three-day project children enter into the world of imagination through the arrival of a teddy bear in their classroom. The project follows through a story-line of events: Who is Teddy?; What Teddy did at school; Teddy goes home to two houses; Our teddies' stories; and Farewell to Teddy.

There are opportunities for children to create a class 'Teddy' album, focusing on the characteristics of their individual teddies, as well as individual teddy-shaped books which can be made based on children's experiences and imagination. These may include 'The day I lost my teddy', 'My teddy was sad' and 'My teddy went on holiday'. This provides an ideal opportunity to discuss titles of stories with the children.

In 'Farewell to Teddy' children select one of the books made to give to Teddy as it moves on. As well as making decisions about the selection of the book, they are encouraged to evaluate the reasons for their choice.

Why this context?

Young children relate well to the teddy-bear theme. Through the context they enter an imaginary world while defining the characteristics of this world and their own bears. Opportunities are provided to explore different places and settings and they are introduced to key elements of the writing process, beginning with a problem: where did the teddy come from?

It offers a variety of opportunities for individual, group and class stories, structured through play activities, real-life experiences and photocopiable sheets. Throughout the project, there is scope for children's writing either to be scribed, word-processed, structured with a 'Teddy' word bank or written by the children themselves. The project can easily be adapted to meet the needs and interests of the youngest and oldest children in the age range.

Project organisation

The project begins with the 'arrival' of the teddy in the class. It may be most suitable to locate the bear in a place which is familiar to the children's routine at the beginning of the day, for example in a cloakroom, in the story corner or sitting on someone's chair. It should immediately raise questions from the teacher and the children: Who is the bear? Where did it come from? Indeed the first activity arises from initial curiosity and questioning. Supported by a photocopiable sheet, this leads to an individual or pair activity based on children's suggestions about the background of the bear.

As the teddy becomes 'integrated' into the routine of the day, decisions are made about what it is going to do. If there is a period of free or structured play, this provides an ideal time for the children to create stories to recall at a feedback session on 'What Teddy did at school today'. Children are encouraged to contribute to class books on this topic.

To maintain the interest in the story-line, a child is nominated to take the teddy home for the night. (Parental involvement is necessary here to inform parents of the purpose and nature of this project.) The child returns the following day, ready to recall the events of the previous evening to the whole class. This leads to the next collaborative class book which outlines the sequence of events.

Publication, celebration and review

The project leads to publication of the children's work in a variety of forms: a teddy album (made by the class), A4-sized individual books, a teddy-shaped class book and zigzag books of Teddy's days at school.

The children's books are read to a parent or other relative at home or on a class or school open day. The adult is asked to complete a photocopiable sheet which asks for a short comment on the story, some memories of his or her own schooldays and for a memory about a favourite toy when he or she was a young child. These adult responses are collated in a class book and placed in the classroom to allow the children to share them and discuss them with their friends.

Books the children may find useful

Hi Bears, Bye Bears, Niki Yektai (1990) Viking
Too Many Teddies, Gus Clarke (1995) Andersen Press
Eddie and Teddy, Gus Clarke (1995) Andersen Press
A Holiday for the Three Bears, Tiny Bradman & Jenny Williams (1995) Collins
It's the Bear, Jez Alborough (1994) Walker
Old Bear and his Friends, Jane Hissey (1991) Red Fox

PRE-SESSION

In preparation for this writing context, supply a teddy bear and enclose a letter (photocopied from page 52) in an envelope marked 'To everyone in Class...' On the morning of session 1, prior to the children's arrival in the classroom, decide on the most appropriate place to leave the bear so that the children can find it. This may be in the cloakroom, or you could place the bear on your chair or a child's chair, in the story corner and so on. Leave the teddy and be prepared to act surprised when the children find it!

1
WHO IS THIS TEDDY?

Teaching content

Creating the stimulus for story-making through the imaginative context of a teddy arriving in the classroom.

What you need

A teddy bear with an envelope containing a letter attached to it (see 'Pre-session'), photocopiable page 53, A3 sheets of paper (prepared with the questions 'Where did the bear come from?' and so on, one question on each sheet, and listed in 'What to do'), six A4 sheets of paper with boxes numbered 1 to 6, writing materials.

What to do

This session begins with the 'discovery' of the teddy bear and involves the whole class gathered together, with attention drawn to the envelope it is holding.

Begin by encouraging the children to talk about the envelope: 'What do you think could be in this envelope? If it is a letter, who sent it?

Why do you think the bear is here?' Open the envelope and either read or ask one of the children to read the letter aloud to the others.

Now ask the children why they think the bear is here for only three days, and what they think should be done with it. At this point it may be worth writing down the children's ideas on an A3 sheet of paper, as this bear is going to be the central character in their story-making.

Finally, encourage children to predict what might happen if the bear does not leave after three days. Ask them to think of any story when something happened because the character did not leave on time, for example, *Cinderella*.

After this preliminary discussion, arrange the class to work in groups of four. Give out copies of photocopiable page 53, one to each group, and ask the children to complete the questions using their own ideas. At a feedback session, when the children have finished, collate their ideas on five sheets of paper:
• Where did the bear come from?
• Who left it in our classroom?
• Why is it here for only three days?
• What will we do with it?
• What do you think will happen if it doesn't leave in three days?

The final part of this session offers the children an opportunity to focus on writing a plan of what the teddy will do for the rest of the day. Tell the children that, in the same groups, you now want them to talk about what they would do with the teddy at this moment, throughout the day and at home time. Ask them to write and draw their ideas on a piece of paper with the title 'Our plan for Teddy'. You may have to scribe for some children, but the main focus is that they see a beginning, middle and end to story-making with the teddy as the central character.

In the last part of this session, the children should come back to the whole group with their plans. As a class, decide on the most popular activities in which Teddy will be involved. Have six A4 sheets of paper prepared and change them horizontally on a wall or display board to show a timeline of Teddy's day.

In the top right-hand corner, briefly write in the plan for each stage of the day, for example sand, weighing, playtime, reading, painting, home time. Tell the children that at the end of the day they will come back to draw the pictures and write about what Teddy did that day at school. Draw an arrow on the first sheet to identify the starting activity and emphasise that all the children will have to share the teddy throughout the day. You may have to allocate tasks or time to ensure fairness, and you will also need to monitor the story-making throughout the day, stopping to ask questions: 'What is Teddy doing now? Does it like weighing? What did it do outside at playtime?' and so on.

2

WHAT TEDDY DID AT SCHOOL TODAY

Teaching content
Recreating the story-making in which children and the teddy were involved through drawings and in written form.

What you need
The six A4 sheets of paper used at the end of session 1 to identify Teddy's plan for the day.

What to do
Towards the end of the day, select one group of six children to draw the events of Teddy's day on the sheets of paper originally used to plan the sequence.

Begin by discussing each part of the day with the whole class, directing questions to the children who were most involved with creating the story at that point of the day. Tell the class that, although six children will be making today's book, there will be opportunities for another two groups to make one for day 2 and day 3. You could then use all of the books created to look at similarities and differences in the stories about Teddy: 'How did this book start? Did Teddy always do the same thing at playtime?' and so on.

The group selected should then each draw one of the pictures for the book. If there is a lot to tell about each episode, you may wish to scribe for the children or supply words as necessary.

At the end of the day, the pictures should be collated into a zigzag book and shown to the rest of the class.

Ask the children to think overnight about a good title for this book about Teddy's first day with the class. On day 2, the book could be finished by selecting the favourite title and choosing two children to design the cover. It should then be placed in an appropriate place within the classroom. Other books and resources on the teddy theme could be placed in the same area.

3

TEDDY GOES HOME TO _____'S HOUSE

Ⓦ ㊺

Teaching content

Continuing the story-line in another setting. Involving family in the development of the story-line.

What you need

Photocopiable page 54, the teddy bear.

What to do

This session contains three linking activities:
• creating a list of what Teddy did on day 1 (whole class);
• 'overnight' activity involving one child's family;
• a small group creating a book about 'What

Teddy did at _____'s house' on day 2.

First, children are required to make a decision based upon what happens to Teddy when they all go home. Hopefully, someone may come up with the solution of taking it home.

Prior to this activity, you will have to seek the participation of families who are willing to carry on this story-line in the evening. It may be necessary to draw names from a 'hat' to ensure fairness, since only two children will be able to have the opportunity to take the bear home during this project.

In this last activity on day 1, the whole class should decide upon the most important things to tell the receiving family about the teddy. These will be characteristics invented by the children through their story-making, for example Teddy doesn't like to get wet, Teddy is happy to have stories read, is always smiling and so on. These should be made into a list and recorded either by you or one of the children on photocopiable page 54.

This list should then be handed over to the

child who is taking the bear home that night, with a reminder that the next morning the child will tell everyone what happened overnight. The parent(s) and the child should record together what Teddy did at _____'s house. The parent(s) may write, while the child draws pictures to bring to school the next day.

Day 2 should begin by the child who took Teddy home recalling what Teddy did at _____'s house. Read, or let the child read, what the parent(s) wrote and let the child show any pictures he or she has drawn. Explain to the children that the writing and the pictures are going to be used as the basis for a house-shaped book entitled 'What Teddy did at _____'s house'. This will be made by a small group of children, led by the child who took the teddy home.

Allocate enough time for the children to see the production of the book through to completion. There will be a need for flexibility based on the children's curiosity and imagination in response to the making of the book.

This activity should be repeated with another family for the evening of day 2.

4

OUR TEDDY ALBUM

Teaching content

Creating a teddy bear story in which individuals draw and write about the characteristics of their own teddy bear.

What you need

Teddy bear album cover, photocopiable pages 55 and 56, children's own teddy bears.

What to do

Prior to this session, ask the children to bring a teddy bear into school. They should be asked to think about what it looks like and to think of a special story about it which they can tell to the whole class.

Begin by gathering all of the children together with their assortment of teddy bears and draw their attention to the differences in size, shape, colour, clothes and so on. Select some children to talk about their own teddy, for example what it looks like, what it feels like, where it came from, and where it has a place in their home. To do this, it may be useful to provide a teddy 'chair' or a teddy 'box' for the child who is talking to use when it is his or her turn. Either the child stands on the box, depending on support, or the teddy sits on it as the child is telling the story.

Give each child a copy of photocopiable page 55. Ask the children to draw a picture of their teddy bear in as much detail as possible

OUR TEDDIES' STORIES

Teaching content

Creating personal stories about children's own teddy bears.

What you need

The children's own teddies, writing and drawing materials.

What to do

This session should take place later in the day, perhaps at the beginning of the afternoon when the children have completed their teddy album. Again, using their own teddy bear, this session offers the opportunity for the children to tell and then write a story involving their own bear.

Begin by seating all of the children at their tables with their teddies. Remind the children that you asked them to think about a special story about their bear. It could be when their bear got lost or went on holiday. Organise the children into pairs and ask them to tell their story to their partner. Some children may tell the story in the third person, some may use the bear as a puppet, and some may use dialogue. When the first child has finished, ask the other child to tell their partner what he or she liked about their story and to ask any questions about it. Children should now exchange roles,

and to write in each of the teddy 'faces', one word to describe their teddy (a total of four words). They should then complete the sheet by writing their teddy's name, where it sleeps, what it likes to do and the name of its best friend. Children should complete this individually, with the teddy bear placed on the table beside them.

When they have finished, organise some time to enable the children to move around each other's tables to view the teddies and to see what the children have written about them. If this is too disruptive, select one group at a time to look at the children's work on the other tables.

Collate the children's individual sheets and use a copy of photocopiable page 56 as a front cover for their stories. The sheets can be stapled, hole-punched, or put into plastic pockets and then into a ring-binder, to be displayed with the teddy album cover in the book corner.

Further development

Record all of the words used to describe the teddies on a class display. This will largely depend on the children's age, ability and motivation for the context.

allowing the other child to tell a story about his or her bear.

Individually, children should now write their story on paper, re-creating it if necessary. If the organisation of this is difficult as a whole class due to numbers, it may be organised by half of the class creating their stories while the others draw a picture of themselves waving goodbye to Teddy, and then swapping over.

Children should decide on a title for their story and design a border for the front cover of their book, not forgetting to write their own name as author. These two-page books can then be placed in plastic pockets, back to back, and collated in a ring-binder with a cover title of 'Our Teddies' Stories'.

These can be shared with another class. The number of different books created at the end of this project also generates a very effective display to which parents or other staff can be invited.

6

FAREWELL TO TEDDY

(W) (30)

Teaching content
Evaluation of the context.

What you need
A display of all books made during the project, photocopiable page 57, wrapping paper, sticky tape, one sheet of A3 paper, writing materials.

What to do
In this last session, the whole class should be gathered together. Read the original letter that Teddy brought and remind the children that it is now time for Teddy to leave, and that when they return tomorrow it won't be there any longer. Discuss the children's feelings at this moment in comparison with how they felt when Teddy arrived. Talk about Teddy's feelings over the three days he has been with them and highlight the range of different emotions.

Encourage the children to select one book which has been written to give to Teddy as a memento of his time with the class. Listen to individual suggestions and encourage the children to tell you why they would choose that book and what they liked best about it.

At the end of this discussion, decide upon one book and wrap it up in front of the children (teddy wrapping paper would be appropriate!). Using photocopiable page 57, ask the children to offer suggestions about what they would like to say to Teddy on his departure. Use a large piece of paper to take suggestions, and then, with the children, select six favourite things to be said. Scribe on the sheet for the children or select individual children to write one each.

This should then be presented to the teddy, along with the book, as the children leave for home. It would be nice if Teddy left a letter of thanks for the children to find the next morning, saying where it was going next, but that's another story!!

7

SHARING THE STORY WITH SOMEONE YOU LOVE

Ⓦ ⏱

Teaching content

Publication, celebration and review. We all have stories about toys when we were young.

What you need

Books written by the children, photocopiable page 58.

What to do

When the stories are complete, make a point of reading them to the class and talking about them with individuals, groups of children and the whole class. Although you will obviously want to ensure that you take time to comment about each book to its author, do not feel that you need to limit your discussion to only stories written by those children to whom you are talking – children can learn a lot from reading each other's work.

When the children's books have been in the classroom for a sufficient length of time, suggest that they are so wonderful that you know the children's parents, or other favourite relatives, would be very keen to see and read them. Arrange for the children to take the books home, or invite the parents into the classroom for a book launch, special assembly or parents' afternoon.

Ask the children what they think their parents or relatives will say about the books they have

written. Do they think that their parents wrote stories like this when they were at school? Do they think they had a teddy bear, or a special toy, when they were children? Introduce a copy of photocopiable page 58. Read through it with the children and explain that it is to be completed by each child's parent, grandparent or other adult who is specially important to the child. Suggest that once completed, the children should bring their sheets (and the books?) back to share with the class.

As the children return with their completed sheets, make a point of talking to the children about what happened when they read their story to their chosen adult. Find out what the adult said about it to the child, what they wrote on their photocopiable sheet and whether they talked to the child about their childhood toys and schooldays. This may be done informally with individuals and groups, or more formally at 'together time' or story time.

Bind the sheets together to make a response book for the story corner. Children will enjoy finding the sheet completed by their own parent and sharing this with their friends.

TEDDY COMES TO SCHOOL

Hello.

I can stay with you

for **3 days** only – not

one minute more.

WHO IS THIS TEDDY?

Where did Teddy come from?

Who left it in our classroom?

Why is it here for only 3 days?

What will we do with it?

What do you think will happen if it doesn't leave in 3 days?

TEDDY GOES HOME

To everyone in _____'s house

Here is a list of important things to note about the bear who has come to visit our classroom:

Thank you for looking after it tonight.

ABOUT MY TEDDY

My teddy looks like this.

Words to describe my teddy:

My teddy is called _____

My teddy sleeps _____

My teddy likes to _____

_____

My teddy's best friend is _____

OUR TEDDY ALBUM

Our
Teddy Album

GOODBYE TEDDY

SHARING THE STORY

Dear adult,
This story has been written in class and its young author has chosen
YOU as the adult they would most like to read it. Please take time to
show your interest and appreciation. We would be very grateful if you
could also answer some of the questions below and explain your
answers to the child. Please make your handwriting as clear as
possible.

Name of child _____ Name of adult _____

What did you like best about this book? Please explain your answer.
Did you ever write books like this when you were at school? Please
explain your answer.

Did you have a favourite toy when you were young? What was it?

Did you ever daydream about your favourite toy? Where did you like to
daydream? Can you remember what happened in your daydreams?

Chapter Six

THE MAGICAL
TRAVEL MACHINE

INTRODUCTION

Project description

In this project the children work in pairs to write a story about two inventor friends who travel on a magical travel machine. They decide where the machine can go and make its control panel. They each draw and write about their own inventor and have some free play with their machine before selecting together the place to which they will go on their first journey.

The children create this place and its inhabitants using a mixture of collage and drawing techniques. Then one child writes about the place and the other writes about the inhabitants and what they are like. The rest of the story is left open for the children to decide what happens. The children take turns with writing and must co-operate to ensure that the illustrations and text tell the rest of the story. The story must end with the inventors using the machine to return home safely.

Why this context?

Children are fascinated by the idea of travelling to magical places and the immense possibilities which this sort of story-line can offer. The project can result in a range of different types of stories – fairy stories, mystery stories and adventure stories – because it allows the children to choose whether to create either lifelike or fantastical places and inhabitants, and lifelike or fantastical main characters.

Children use place, setting and character to structure and drive the story-line. Because the story is a joint effort, it requires good co-operation but also offers a high degree of support as children work together to generate and develop ideas.

Project organisation

The children work in the same pairs throughout the project. They do most work together – making the control panel, creating the place and writing the final part of the story, but they also produce individual pieces of work when creating and writing about the inventors.

Publication, celebration and review

The book is written on A4-sized paper, turned sideways (landscape) and stapled within a larger cover. The control panel forms the cover illustration, with strips above and below for the title and name of the authors.

The books can be displayed in the classroom and shared with other children in the class. After one week each pair has to meet with another pair to share and read their books and to talk about the type of story they have written. The whole class then complete an evaluation sheet on each of the two books they have seen during this lesson.

Books the children may find useful

Any books that describe imaginary lands or unusual places in an evocative way, or that describe the inhabitants could be used. For example:

Incredible Adventures of Professor Brainestawm, Norman Hunter (1992) Puffin
Tigerella, Kit Wright (1993) Scholastic
Where the Wild Things Are, M. Sendak (1992) Picture Lions
We're Going on a Bear Hunt, M. Rosen & H. Oxenbury (1993) Walker Books
Mog in the Fog, H. Nicoll & J. Pienokowski (1984) Puffin
Beware, Beware, Susan Hill (1993) Walker Books
Ned and the Joybaloo, Hiawyn Oram (1992) Andersen Press
Professor Puffendorf's Secret Potion, Korky Paul and Robin Tzannes (1995) Oxford University Press
The Mice and the Travel Machine, Rodney Peppe (1986) Puffin
The Mice and the Clockwork Bus, Rodney Peppe (1988) Puffin
The Mice and the Flying Basket, Rodney Peppe (1988) Puffin

Some time before this context, read the children as many stories as possible about wonderful places, inventors and machines. (See the list of recommended books on the opposite page.)

MAGICAL PLACES FOR MYSTERIOUS TRAVEL

Teaching content

Discussion can help to generate ideas; no two magical places are the same; the reader needs to know what makes this place special.

What you need

Photocopiable page 66, writing and drawing materials, chalkboard.

What to do

Put the children into pairs. Tell them that they are going to design and make the control panel of a magical travel machine which will be able to take them to any magic land that they would like to go. Explain that, once made, each pair will invent and write a story about their machine, but first they must decide on the places to which their machine can travel.

Brainstorm a class list of exciting, magical or mysterious places. The children may suggest the moon, a magic star, an enchanted wood, a secret cave, a castle, a treasure island, the North Pole, the jungle, a pirate ship, a deserted city, the bottom of the sea, a land where they can control the weather, a dragon's mountain, a cup final football pitch, a land in which they, or its inhabitants, are invisible, a land made of jelly, or a scene from a favourite story or television programme.

Allow ten minutes for the pairs to discuss and decide on four places that they would like their own machine to visit. Ask the children to record their decisions by drawing them on to the photocopiable page. Explain that no two places are ever exactly the same and that while they draw they should be thinking and talking about what makes *this* place – *this* particular desert island or undersea world – different and

special. Finally, ask them to write key words or phrases to describe these special features. These might include the objects, sounds or atmosphere of each of the places that they have drawn.

End the session by explaining that tomorrow the children will make the control panel for their machine.

MAKING THE CONTROLS

Teaching content

Describing sound and motion to create atmosphere.

What you need

Completed photocopiable page 66, photocopiable pages 67 and 68, A4 card, scissors, glue, craft materials, pens, paper fasteners, scrap paper, sticky tape.

What to do

Introduce the session by reminding the children of the destinations that they chose on photocopiable page 66 for their magical travel machine. Explain that they must now make the control panel for the machine. Ask the children to work in the same pairs as before. Show them how they can use a copy of photocopiable page 67 as a resource bank of ideas for making moving dials and scales. Explain that photocopiable sheet 68 contains a selection of pointers, scales and dials that they may like to copy, or cut out and mount on card to use in making their own control panel.

Explain that the control panel is the most important part of the machine. Before they start, the children must decide which dials and switches they will have on their panel; which ones will be used to turn the machine on and

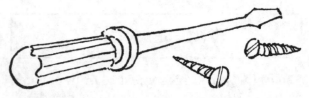

off, select a destination, go on a journey and return. Explain that each dial and switch must have a purpose and control something in the machine and that it must all fit on to the A4 card with room for the destination labels.

Show the children how to cut out and use their pictures and the place descriptors from photocopiable page 66 to make the destination labels for the controls. The children may find it useful to have scrap paper to draw, explain or record their initial ideas. In this way the children will jointly negotiate and decide on what their machines can do.

As the children work, encourage them to talk about the sort of noises their machine makes as the various controls are pressed and about the sensations that anyone travelling in the machine would experience as it begins its magical journey.

Once the control panel has been made, the children should write a brief set of instructions about how to use it. These will eventually form page 1 of the book, but they could be displayed temporarily in the classroom beside the control panel to which they refer.

INVENTORS

Teaching content
Creating and describing characters; thinking beyond stereotypes.

What you need
Paper rectangles pre-cut to A6 size, photocopiable page 69, collage, drawing and writing materials, glue, scissors, chalkboard.

What to do
Introduce the session by explaining that the children now need to think about the key characters in their story. Each child is going to draw and name one of the two friends who invented and made this magical travel machine. Tell the children to think very carefully about the characters they are going to create and explain that, although these people will be friends, they will not be identical.

Explain that inventors do not need to always look like a typical 'mad scientist' with frizzy hair and glasses. Their inventors could be male or female and may be very old or about the children's own age. They may have a touch of magic about them (a magician or wizard?), be very rich and invent things as a hobby, or be very poor (having spent their last pennies on this project). Or maybe their inventors will be a bit like themselves or a person they know.

Give out the A6 paper and collage/drawing materials but, before they begin, tell the children to think about the following (list them on the board):
• overall appearance – smart or untidy? Are their clothes new or old, trendy, old-fashioned or 'magical' in some way?
• typical facial expression – do they tend to frown with concentration, giggle, smile quietly to themselves, shout or get angry quickly?
• what the character is like as a person – what they enjoy or hate doing;
• which destinations they would particularly like to visit.

While the children work, encourage them to talk in their pairs about these questions and also about:
• how their two characters met;
• what their characters like to do together;
• whether their characters ever argue, and if so, what about;
• what their characters like and admire about each other.

Encourage the children to help each other with ideas and to choose an appropriate name for each character. Once finished, the children should be given time to show and talk about their characters with their partner.

Give out copies of photocopiable page 69 and tell the children to help each other to complete the speech bubbles, showing what their characters say to each other as they gaze at their magical travel machine.

Ask the children to arrange and paste their characters and speech bubbles on to two blank sheets of A4 paper. These will eventually function as a double-page spread of the book and must therefore have the same orientation as the control panel which will form its cover.

Tell the children to write the name and a brief description of what the character is like as a person underneath each picture. Some children may prefer to write this on separate paper and paste it into position.

MAGIC PLAY ON THE MAGIC MACHINES

†† ⟳

Teaching content

Developing story-lines through unstructured talk/play.

What you need

Machine controls made by the children.

What to do

Once children have made their machines and invented their main characters, it is profitable to allow a short period for children to simply talk about, adapt and play with their machines, informally inventing and developing their own stories. This will generate ideas that can later feed the writing process.

Many children will happily invent different stories about their characters and the places they go. A few children may get stuck, with the same story (usually beginning and ending with a fight between the goodies and the baddies) taking place in each of the places. If this happens, it can be useful to prompt the play to take a different course by suggesting different categories of events that could happen: they could find something; meet someone; have an accident; lose something; the weather could change; something magical could happen.

OFF WE GO!

†† ⏱30

Teaching content

Writing dialogue and using it to move the story forward.

What you need

Writing materials (including A4 paper), chalkboard.

What to do

Ask the children to look together at their control panel and to decide what happens when their two characters make the first journey.
• Where do they decide to go?
• Which character sets the controls, or do they both do it?
• What happens? What does it feel like as the machine starts to work?
• What do their characters say to each other? What do they say to themselves?

Give the children a few minutes to discuss these questions in their pairs and then give them A4 paper and ask them to write a short conversation about what the characters say to each other as they set the machine to work. You may need to explain briefly some of the conventions of writing dialogue and to suggest that the children take turns in writing – while one writes the other should help by suggesting words, spellings or ideas.

Finally, put the following sentence on the board, and ask the children to copy and complete it at the bottom of the dialogue they have written: 'We knew the machine had started to work because...'

End the session by telling the children that tomorrow they will be asked to draw a joint picture of the place they go to and who lives there – creature or human. Ask the children to think about what the two inventors could see, who they could meet and what could happen when the machine lands and to discuss it whenever they have an odd moment at playtime.

THE MAGICAL PLACE

WHAT HAPPENS?

Teaching content

Describing place through scenery and inhabitants.

What you need

Writing materials (including A4 paper and scrap paper), drawing and collage materials.

What to do

Remind the children of the brief descriptor they have already written about this place. Give each pair an A4 sheet and small scraps of paper. Tell the children to work together to draw the place and its inhabitants on the A4 paper. Show the children how they can use the separate scraps of paper and sticky tape to make lift-the-flap doors to hide the inhabitants from immediate view. Explain that, as they draw, the children must decide what the inhabitants are like (friendly, curious, shy, funny, hostile...) and how they would react to strangers.

When the children have finished, call the class together and ask some pairs to share their work. Explain that each child in the pair is now going to write a separate part of the story. One child is going to write a short description of the place, including details of its atmosphere and physical features. This may involve describing:
• what the two inventors see, hear, smell and touch in this place;
• what the inventors say to each other about this place.

The other child is going to write a short piece about the inhabitants. This may describe:
• what they are called;
• what they look like;
• how they communicate;
• their attitude to newcomers – what they would say, think or do.

Then ask the children to cut out and paste their work on to a single page or, if they have written more than will fit on to a single page, present it as two A4 pages.

Finally, tell the children that tomorrow they will be asked to write about what happens when their characters meet the inhabitants. Ask them to think about this and try to plan how their story will end.

Teaching content

Choosing how the story moves forward; sequencing the story development; using pictures and text to move the story forward.

What you need

Writing and drawing materials, A4 paper.

What to do

Remind the children of the characters, the place and its inhabitants that they have already created. Explain that this is the last part of the book and the children must decide the rest of the story. Suggest that they work together, taking turns to be the scribe. The child who is not holding the pencil should help the writer with ideas about what to say, spelling and so on. Once both have taken a turn at writing, they may choose to do an illustration, either jointly or separately, on one of the smaller pieces of paper. Explain that this may help them to think of the next part of the story.

Depending on the class, it may be wise to make certain stipulations: for example, that the story cannot contain any fighting, the characters have to return to earth, the story must have a happy ending, the story should be a particular length, or certain parts of the story may be told in pictures.

Show the children the paper and materials for the illustrations. Explain that they must decide when and how to illustrate the story, but emphasise the importance of taking equal responsibility for the illustrations and writing.

When the children have written their stories, tell them that tomorrow they will collate the pages for the book and make the control panel into its front cover. Suggest that before then, each pair should discuss and decide on a book title. Remind them that the title should tell the reader something about the story and may also indicate what sort of story it is.

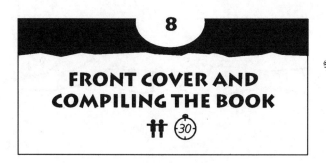

8

FRONT COVER AND COMPILING THE BOOK
†† ⏱30

Teaching content
Titles tell the reader something about the story. They are easy to see on the front cover.

What you need
Card or sugar paper folded to make a slightly larger than A4 front/back cover for each book, paper strips for the title and the authors' names, glue, stapler, chalkboard, writing and drawing materials.

What to do
Show the children how their control panel will be mounted on to sugar paper or card and will form the cover illustration for their book. Ensure that there is enough space at the top and bottom of the cover for the strips of paper which have the title and authors' names.

Tell the children to decide on a title for their story. Point out that titles must be short, easy to read and tell the reader something about the story. One child should write the title and the other the names of the authors on to the paper strips. Explain that they may need to practise writing so that the letters fit neatly and evenly on to the paper.

When they are both happy with the lettering of both title and authors, they should glue these into place on the front cover.

Finally, show the children how to collate and check the sequences of their pages, numbering and stapling them together between the front

and back cover. The children may find the following sequence helpful (listed on the board):

Front cover:	Control panel
Page 1	Instructions for control panel
Pages 2 & 3	The inventors and speech bubbles
Page 4	Off we go! Conversation as the machine takes off
Page 5	Place picture
Page 6 (& 7)	Place writing
Page 7	What happens

9

CELEBRATION AND REVIEW
††-†††† ⏱

Teaching content
Celebration of completed books.

What you need
Photocopiable page 70, writing materials.

What to do
Display the books in the classroom for about a week. Then put pairs together to form groups of four. Tell each pair to show and read their book to the other two children. Once both pairs have seen both books, the whole group of children should be asked to complete one evaluation sheet for each book (which you have photocopied from page 70).

MAGICAL PLACES FOR MYSTERIOUS TRAVEL

Our magical travel machine could take us to:

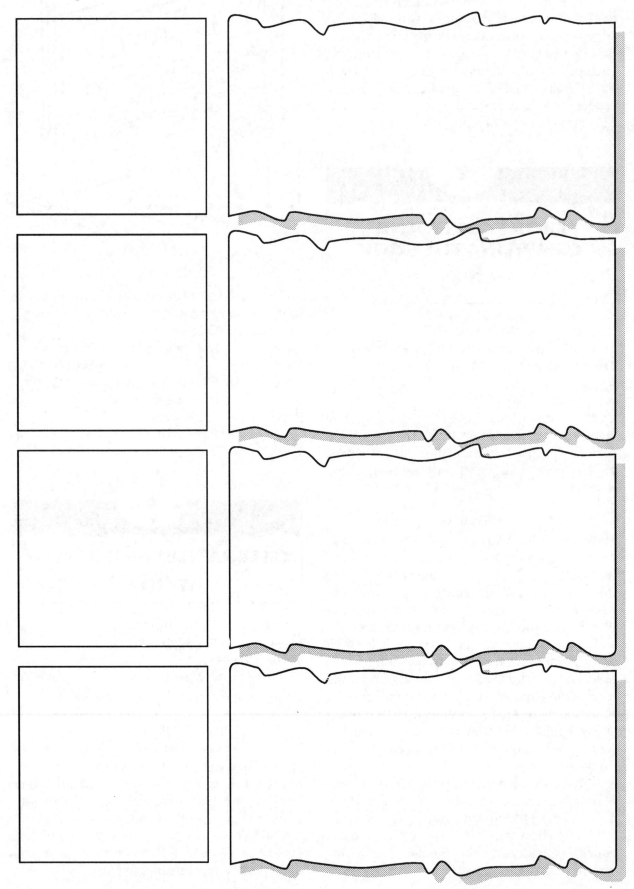

Scholastic
IMAGINATIVE WRITING
Workshop

MAKING THE CONTROLS

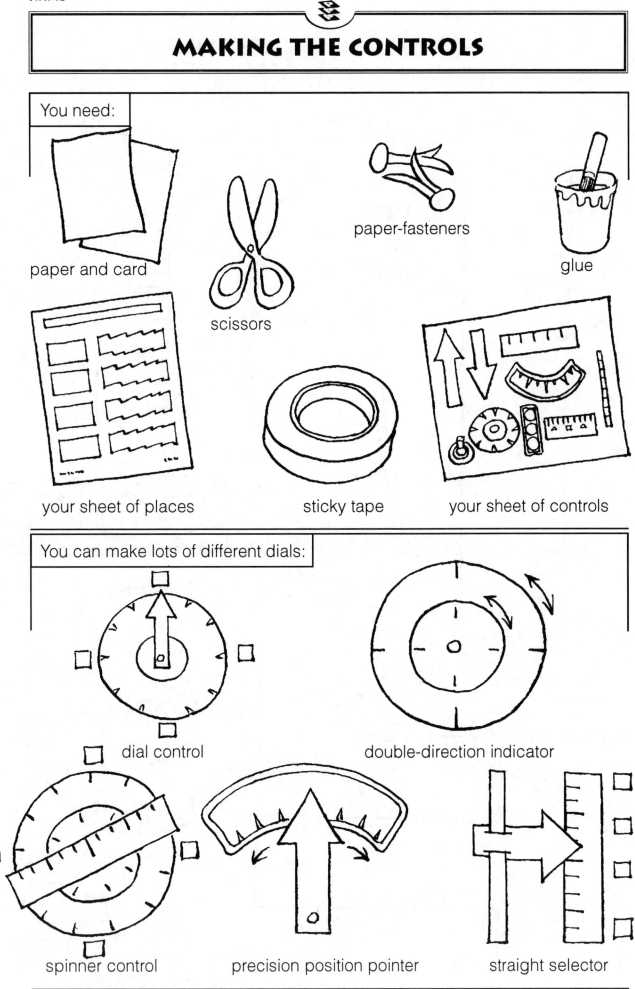

You need:

paper and card

scissors

paper-fasteners

glue

your sheet of places

sticky tape

your sheet of controls

You can make lots of different dials:

dial control

double-direction indicator

spinner control

precision position pointer

straight selector

MAKING THE CONTROLS

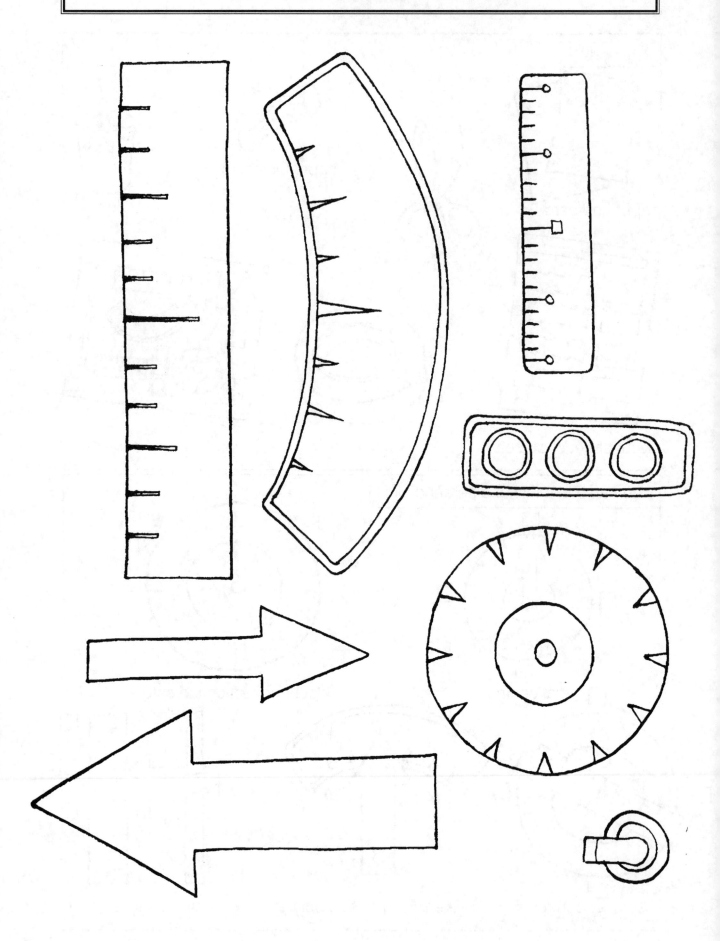

INVENTORS

CELEBRATION AND REVIEW

◆ How would you describe this story?

◆ What did you think of the front cover and presentation?

◆ Which bits of the story are best to read? Why?

◆ Did you enjoy talking about this story? Why?

Scholastic
WRITING
Workshop

Chapter Seven

OH NO, BABY!

INTRODUCTION

Project description

In this project the children work in groups of four to make a large (A3-sized) 'lift-the-flap book' about a baby who hides an important object somewhere in the house.

The project begins with the children thinking about babies in general and they are encouraged to find out stories about themselves as babies. Each group is given a photocopiable sheet which provides a focus for discussing and naming the baby who will be the main character of their story. This photocopiable sheet forms the first page of the book. The children are told that the baby has hidden or lost something. The group decide on the object that is missing and on the family member who discovers it has gone. They record *exactly* what was said at that point on a large speech bubble. Each group is given five photocopiable sheets of different rooms in a house. Each child in the group takes responsibility for a different room and must find four places in the room where the object *could* be hidden. They cut around each place to make 'lift-the-flap' mechanisms. Above each flap they write 'Is it in/under/behind the...' and behind the flap they write 'No, not there'. It is decided in which room the object will finally be found and in this instance the child draws the object and writes 'Yes – at last' behind one flap. A word bank (also on a photocopiable sheet) is provided to support this writing.

Once the pictures have been coloured and mounted, the group decide how best to sequence them to make the story flow. They invent a title for their story and make the front and back cover.

Why this context?

Children, especially young children, are interested and knowledgeable about babies. Many will have younger brothers and sisters and all will remember, or be able to ask their parents about, what they were like when they were small.

This context provides an example of a structure-driven story, where the framework of the story is predetermined by a structured format based on the rooms of the house. Children will have encountered many similar formats in their reading.

The highly structured writing frame gives support to young children, who are just beginning to write. The context provides sufficient support to enable most of them to do this independently. It also encourages them to use both text and pictures to create settings and move the story-line forward.

Finally, the context requires the children to decide on the best sequence of events for their story, and this raises issues about structuring the story to create a long, slow build-up while looking for the lost object. Children quickly realise that if they sequence the story so that the object is found in the room on the first page there is no incentive for the reader to read to the end.

Project organisation

Both the writing demands and the collaborative demands of this project are relatively straightforward. The children work in groups of five and take simple key decisions (about the name of the baby, what was lost or hidden and who was looking for it) as a group. The most complex group decision concerns the final sequence of the pages.

The written work is largely individual and is supported by photocopiable sheets. This makes the project especially suitable for younger children.

Publication, celebration and review

The book is published as a 'lift-the-flap' book on A3-sized paper. The books are shared with the class and displayed in the class or school library. Children are encouraged to read the books created by other groups and to complete a 'prediction' sheet which can be stored in an envelope attached to the back cover.

Books the children may find useful

Books that provide a platform for talking about babies, and what they can be like. Also, any books that illustrate a structure driven story-line, or have lift-the-flap mechanisms.
Mog and the Baby, Judith Kerr (1992) Picture Lions
Going Swimming (1990) and *Doing the Garden* (1992) by Sarah Garland, Puffin
Who's a Clever Baby Then?, David McKee (1988) Andersen Press
On Friday Something Funny Happened, John Prater (1992) Oliver & Boyd
Nicky's Noisy Night, H. Ziefert (1986) Puffin
The Baby's Catalogue, Janet and Allan Ahlberg (1995) Puffin

PRE-SESSION

Preparation for this project involves the children thinking and talking about babies. Any of the following activities will help to get the children into a 'baby mood' and generate interest in writing a baby story:

• photographs of the children when they were babies;

• stories from parents about the children as babies;

• a visit by a baby to the classroom;

• the play area set up as a baby clinic;

• collections of baby clothes and equipment;

• stories about babies (see list on opposite page).

1
MEET OUR BABY
ŤŤŤŤ ⏱40

Teaching content
Creating character through actions.

What you need
Photocopiable pages 77 and 78 (both enlarged to A3 size – one set per group), paper squares approx 10cm x 12cm, writing and drawing materials, scissors, glue.

What to do
Introduce the lesson by asking the children to tell you about babies. Ask questions which generate discussion about:

• babies' daily routines – where they sleep, what they eat, the toys they play with;

• what they can do and cannot do – how they move about;

• what parents say to babies and to each other about babies – what babies 'say' and do to parents.

Put the children into groups of five and give each group a copy of photocopiable page 77, enlarged to A3 size. Briefly explain that, later on, the children will be asked to give this baby a name, but first they have to think carefully about what the baby is like. Give the groups a few minutes to discuss and decide whether this baby is male or female and how old it is.

Read out one of the starter sentences for the annotated drawing on the photocopiable sheet. Ask the children to talk in their groups about how they could complete it. When each group has had some time to discuss possible answers, ask them to share their suggestions briefly with the class. Ask one child from each group to write the group's answer on the sheet.

Do the same for other starter sentences on the photocopiable sheet, choosing a different 'scribe' each time.

Tell the children that the baby has no name and give each group a few minutes to decide what they will call the baby. When all the group members agree, tell them to write the baby's name in the space provided.

Finally, ask the whole class to suggest different things which this baby might like to play with. Give each group a copy of photocopiable page 78 and each child a small piece of paper. Ask the children to draw one toy for the baby. These toys should be cut out and pasted on to the toy-box pictured on the photocopiable sheet.

End the session by telling the children that this particular baby likes to hide things but can never find them again. Ask the children to find out, by asking their parents, whether they were ever like that as young children. If so, what sort of things did they like to hide, and where?

MISSING – LOST OR HIDDEN?

卌-† 🔟

Teaching content

A 'problem' that drives the story; brainstorming as a technique for generating and selecting ideas; adding details to settings.

What you need

Photocopiable page 79 (enlarged to A3 size – one per child), photocopiable pages 80 to 84 (one A4 set per group), chalkboard, A3 paper, scissors, glue, photocopiable page 31.

What to do

Start the session by telling the children that something terrible has happened. The baby has lost or hidden something very important. What could it be? Brainstorm ideas with the class, writing a list on the board. If the children find it difficult to come up with ideas, use the following prompt questions to help them:
• Is it something the baby needs?
• Is it something belonging to the baby's mother?
• Is it something belonging to the baby's father?
• Is it something belonging to another child?
• Is it something belonging to a pet in the house?

Ask the children to work in their original groups and give each group a few minutes to decide what it is that the baby has lost, and who notices it missing. What does that person say?

Give each group a large speech bubble (photocopied, enlarged if necessary, and cut out from page 31) and ask the children to write in it exactly what was said when the object was discovered missing. Some groups may want to write several of these.

Give a copy of photocopiable page 79 to each child and explain that this is an outline of a room in the baby's house. Give out copies of photocopiable pages 80 to 84 (one set per group). Explain that each child must choose a different room to make by cutting and pasting the furniture tabs on to the room outline. Ask the children to identify the furniture for each room and talk about why the baby may have been in that room recently.

Tell the class that each group is going to write a story about how the lost object gets found. The object has been hidden by the baby in one of the rooms.

Tell the children to look carefully at the furniture for the room they have chosen. Where could the object be hidden? Take suggestions from the class. Could it be behind a cushion, in a cupboard, under something? Point out the tab on each piece of furniture. Show the children how to cut around each object, put glue on the tab and stick it in place on the room outline to make a flap that lifts up. Then, show the

children how to add additional details for their room, drawing them directly on to the photocopied sheet. Encourage the children to think about their rooms at home and add as many details as possible. If the children do this carefully, they will have cushions, mats and rugs that can be lifted up, cupboards that can be opened, and drawers and chairs that can be moved.

When the children have coloured their rooms, store the sheets carefully so that they can be completed in the next session. End by telling the children that in the next session they will find out in which room the object has been hidden.

3

HIDING THE OBJECT

卄卄-† (40)

Teaching content
What the reader knows (or doesn't know!).

What you need
A3 rooms from previous session, photocopiable page 85, collage materials, scissors, writing and drawing materials (including slips of paper).

What to do
Put the children to work in the same groups as before. Explain that the groups must now decide in which room the object has been hidden. This can be done:
• by mutual consent – the children within a group all agree on one room in which the object will be hidden behind one of the 'lift-the-flap' mechanisms;
• by a 'lucky draw' in which group members put their name into a 'hat'. The person whose name is drawn out hides the object in their room.

Give the children their sheets from the previous session. Explain that, although the children now know in which room the object has been hidden, it could be under any one of the pieces of furniture that have been cut out. Explain that each group must keep the whereabouts of their object a secret from the other groups.

On their sheets which were completed in the previous session, show the children how to write either:
'Is it behind the...' or 'Is it under the...' as appropriate above each 'flap', and then how to write on the inside 'No, not there'. Photocopiable page 85 provides a word bank for this activity.

The child who has the object hidden in his or her room will draw the object under one flap, and write 'Yes – at last'.

For the remainder of the session, let the children finish colouring their pictures and show them how to use bits of collage materials to make a cheerful border around the edge of their picture.

4

COMPILING THE BOOK

卌 ③⓪

Teaching content

Sequencing a story; building suspense; information on a front cover and design of a front cover.

What you need

Work completed so far, staplers, A3-sized card in various colours, glue, narrow strips of paper, writing and drawing materials (including thick marker pens).

What to do

Each group should now have:
• a completed A3 photocopiable sheet headed 'Meet our baby';
• a completed A3 photocopiable sheet of the toy-box;
• at least one completed speech bubble saying exactly what was said when it was discovered that the object was missing;
• five A3 pictures of different rooms with flaps cut out and writing above and inside all the flaps.

Ask each group to decide how they think these individual pages should be sequenced to tell the story in as clear and exciting a way as possible. You may like to raise the following issues:
• Do they need to give any additional information to make the story more complete? The children will probably point out the need to complete the box at the bottom of the toy-box picture. Ask the children to write in this any additional information they think might be important.
• What is the best page sequence for the rooms? From the reader's point of view, what would happen if the object were 'discovered' before all the rooms had been visited?

Point out that the book needs a front and back cover and show the children the card you have prepared. Allow each group to choose a colour. Discuss the information that can be found on all front covers, and how it is usually laid out. Explain how the title and the illustration on the front cover of a book should be appropriate to the story. Give each group a short while to decide on a title for their book.

Show them how to write a title on a separate piece of paper and then paste this on to their cover. Suggest they draw some illustrations to complete their cover.

Finally, put the pages in sequence inside the cover and staple them all together. Display the books in the reading corner of the classroom.

5

SHARING THE STORIES

卌十 ⑮

Teaching content

Celebration and enjoyment of finished product.

What you need

Books made by each group, photocopiable page 86, large envelopes.

What to do

At together time, make opportunities for each group of children to present the books they have made to the class. Encourage the children to comment on what they most enjoy about them, and on what they enjoyed about making them. Explain that you will paste an envelope on the inside back cover of each book. Suggest that, before reading a book displayed in the library, the children complete the first half of the photocopiable sheet and the second half once they have read it. They can then place the folded sheet in the envelope at the back of the book.

MEET OUR BABY

This baby's name is

This baby likes to think about...

This baby likes to listen to...

This baby likes to say...

This baby likes to grab...

This baby likes to...

THE BABY'S TOY-BOX

The baby's toy-box.
But what *this* baby really
likes is...

MISSING – LOST OR HIDDEN?

Is it in the...

THE BATHROOM

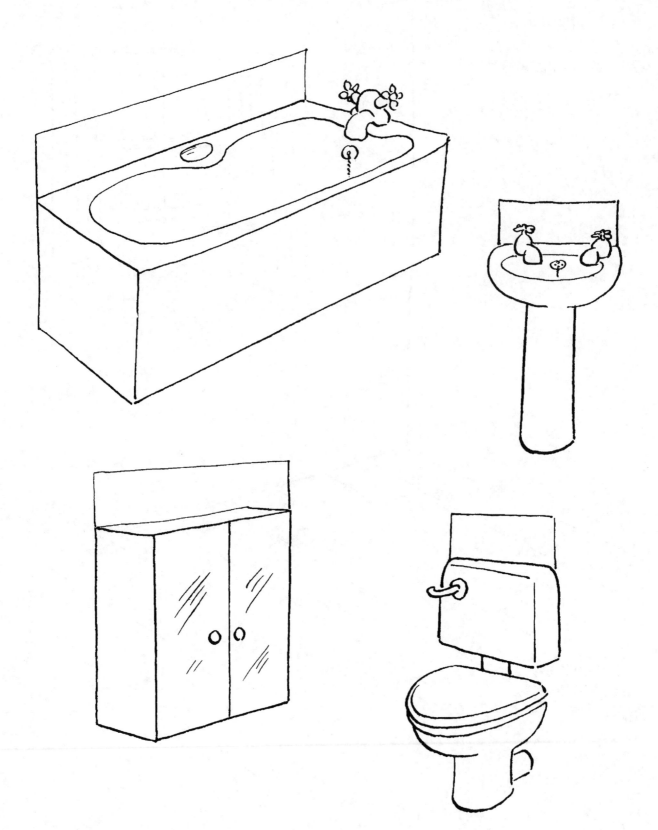

Scholastic
IMAGINATIVE WRITING
Workshop

THE KITCHEN

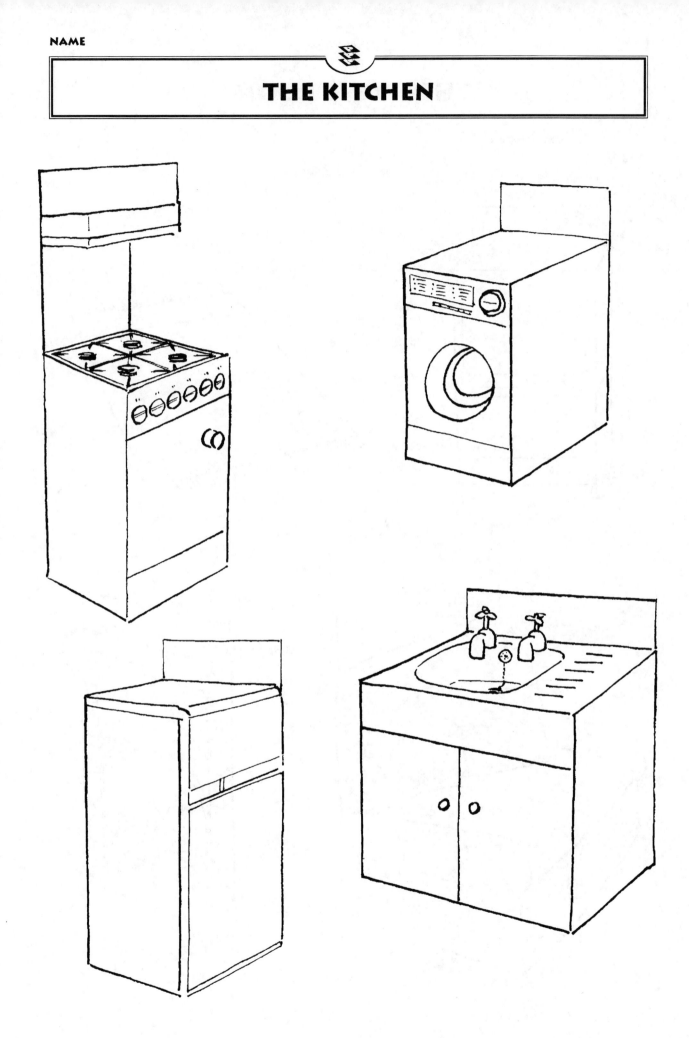

THE LIVING ROOM

THE BABY'S ROOM

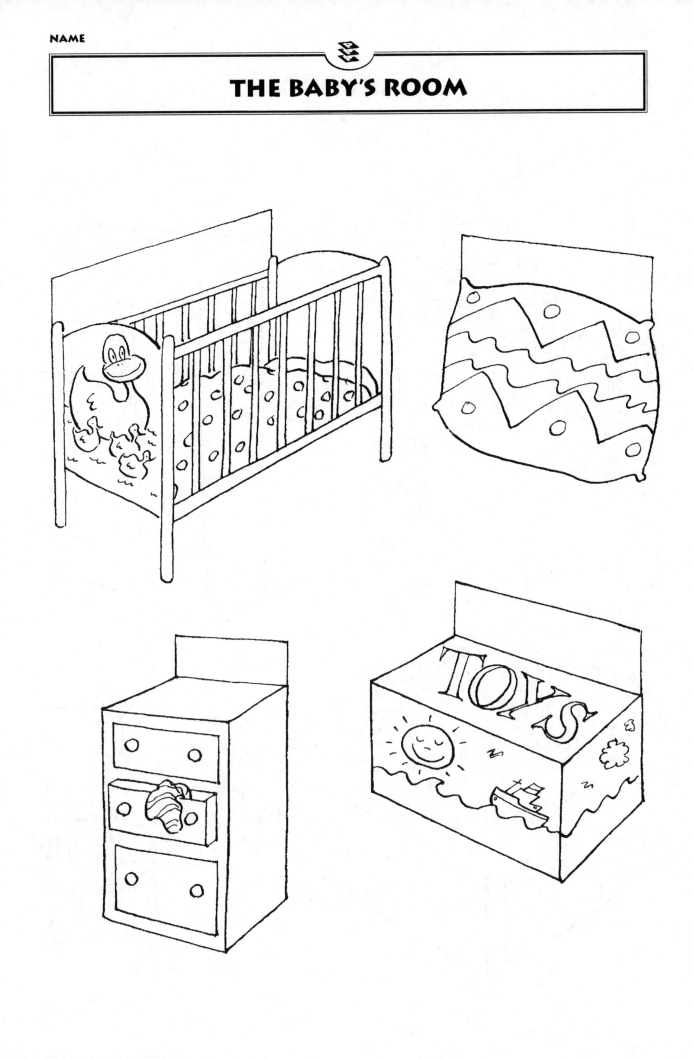

THE BEDROOM

WORD BANK

	bath		fridge
	bed		loo
	chair		mat
	cooker		sink
	cot		sofa
	cupboard		toy-box
	cushion		TV
	drawers		wardrobe
	dressing-table		wash-basin
	fireplace		washing machine

SHARING THE STORIES

Do you think it will be hidden in (tick one):

the bathroom?

the living room?

the bedroom?

the baby's room?

the kitchen?

Were you right (tick one)?

Yes   No

Name _____

Chapter Eight

ZIGZAG ROBOTS

INTRODUCTION

Project description

In this project pairs of children write a joint story about the meeting of two robots. The project begins with individual work when each child invents and makes a robot character. They write a short description of their robot before telling a partner about the robot they have made. The children help their partners to finish the last part of the robot descriptions.

The children are told to imagine that their robots meet. Each pair has to discuss what this meeting is like. The children take it in turns to write the story, with the 'non-writer' suggesting ideas, helping with spelling and generally giving prompts to carry the work forward. In the final writing session, the children have to decide what their robots do together and how their story ends. Again, this is a shared writing task with children taking turns at writing and supporting.

Finally, the children work in pairs to mount and sequence their book into a six-page zigzag book. They devise a title for the book and design a front cover. The work is shared in groups of four, with each pair reading their story to the other pair, who complete an evaluation sheet. Books are also displayed on a rotational basis in the class library.

Why this context?

Children enjoy walking and talking like robots and are fascinated by their potential for doing all sorts of superhuman things. The individual robot-making and writing sessions at the start of the project ensure that every child is involved and that they all have ideas to bring to the collaborative paired work that follows.

Working in pairs supports children during the composing process, as they develop the plot out of the characters they have each devised. It also provides help and support to children who find the scribing aspect of writing off-putting. Tasks that may be difficult to do alone are often quite fun to do with a friend. This can be a powerful form of support for children who feel isolated and under pressure when they are asked to write and is a good way of developing positive attitudes to writing.

Finally, this context offers the children direct instruction and experience of book-making and effective presentation. They are given limited, but important, opportunities for choosing how their book will look, which adds to their sense of control and ownership.

Project organisation

It is important that children have had sufficient time to invent their own robots before sharing these with their partners. Because the rest of the project involves children collaborating quite closely, it is a good idea for the children to work in friendship pairs.

Publication, celebration and review

The work is published in the form of an A4-sized zigzag book. The children are given choices about the colour scheme and play a central role in making the book. The work is shared in groups of six to eight, with each pair reading their story to the rest of the group. Books are also displayed on a rotational basis in the class library. This helps to sustain interest and discussion of the books for longer, and can encourage children to read more than they would were several versions to be placed in the library at the same time. It also allows the teacher to 'spotlight' particular stories during 'together times' over the course of a fortnight, which further helps to maintain interest.

Books the children may find useful

Any books that illustrate characters with strong and different personalities that could be used to spark ideas for the children's robots. For example:

Elvira the Dragon Princess, Margaret Shannon (1993) Hippo Books

The Paper-bag Princess, Robert Munsch (1991) Scholastic

Simpkin, Quentin Blake (1993) Jonathan Cape

'The Snowman' in *Stories for Six-Year-Olds*, edited by Sara and Stephen Corrin (1981) Puffin

Patch the Pirate Cat, Andrew Martyr (1983) Transworld Publications

1

SPECIAL ROBOTS
✝ 45

Teaching content
Creating a character; characterisation through speech, appearance and actions.

What you need
Collage materials, gummed paper, shapes, sequins, wool, wood, material, scissors, glue, A5 card in a variety of colours (including black and white), chalkboard/A3 sheet of paper with key questions listed, writing and drawing materials (including blank paper for word bank).

What to do
Explain to the children that they are going to make a zigzag robot from the collage materials. Tell them that their robot will be different from any other robot that has ever existed because they are going to make it different. Show the children the card, drawing and collage materials and explain that they may use any of these to create their robot.

Tell the children to think carefully about the sort of robot they want to make and then choose an appropriate colour of card on which to make it. Explain that they may, for example, choose different colours for a happy robot, a smart robot, a streetwise robot, a busy robot or a shy robot. Try not to direct this so closely, however, that you end up suggesting appropriate colours for each one.

Explain that the children must decide the basic shape of their robots and, in doing this, should consider the following:
• Will it have a separate or combined head and body?
• How will it move – will it have wheels? If so, are they like a car or a vacuum cleaner? Will it have legs? (If so, how many?) Or maybe it hovers, springs, or slides.
• How will it communicate – will it have a mouth, lights, make 'beeping' sounds?

Give the children their chosen colour of card and explain that they may use it lengthways or widthways, but their robot should be large enough to fill most of the paper.

Before the children start their work, explain that it may take a while to make their robot and

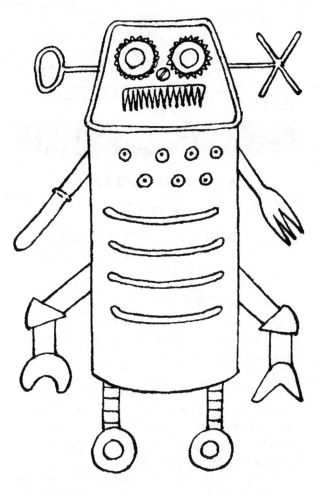

while they work they should consider the following questions. (List these on the board or on an A3 sheet of paper so that the children can refer to them.)
• What is the name of your robot?
• How does it speak?
• What does it like to talk about?
• What needs to be done to it to keep it in good condition?
• Why was it built? What is it very good at doing?
• Where does it live?

As the children work, go around the class talking to them about their robot and what makes it special. Make a point of talking to those children whom you know sometimes find it difficult to think of ideas for stories. Note down any vocabulary which you think may be useful and use this to construct a word bank.

When the robots have been made, choose a few children to show their work to the class and talk about what their robot is like. End the activity by telling the children that in the next session they will write about their robots. Suggest that they think and talk about them at home that evening. Collect the robots in at the end of the session.

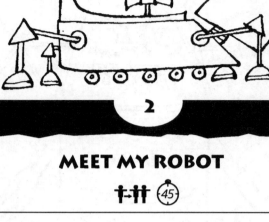

2

MEET MY ROBOT

† †-†† (45)

Teaching content
Describing a character.

What you need
Word bank of key vocabulary from session 1, questions from session 1, writing materials, paper smaller than A4.

What to do
Remind the children of the robots they drew in the previous session and give them out. Go over the questions that the children had to consider while making them.

Give out the writing materials and tell the children that they have a short time to write about their robot. Explain that they may use the key questions from the previous session to help them to get started. If they answer some of these, they will have the beginning of a good description. Point out the word bank and read through it with the children.

Now give the children time to write. Tell the children that if some aspects of their robots are obvious, for example how the robot moves, then they do not have to write about these. When they have nearly finished their writing, ask the children to work with a partner of their choice. Give them six to eight minutes (three or four minutes each) to show and tell their partner about their robot. Be quite strict about the swap-over time – it is vital that each child has an opportunity to hear about the other robot. Give the pairs time to read both pieces of writing together. Suggest that now they know a bit about each other's robot they will be able to help each other decide what sort of personality each robot has. Suggest the children help each other to add a short piece about each robot's personality to the end of the descriptions. If necessary, model how to do this. Explain that sometimes it is as helpful to ask questions as it is to suggest what should be written down.

3

NICE TO MEET YOU!

†† (30)

Teaching content
Using dialogue to advance the story-line; characterisation through speech.

What you need
Writing materials, paper smaller than A4.

What to do
Ask the children to work in the same pairs as before. Tell the children that the story of their robots is not yet finished. Explain that one day their two robots meet. Give the children a short while to discuss what happens at this meeting. They may find the following questions helpful:
• Where do your robots meet?
• What are they each doing when they meet?
• What do they like about each other?
• What do they say to each other?

Give each pair one sheet of paper and explain that you want them to work together to write about this meeting. Each child should take it in turns to write, with the non-writing child helping by suggesting what to say and giving advice on spelling and so on. The children should try to ensure that each partner does *some* writing and *some* suggesting. (Depending on the pairs, it may be appropriate to decree that each child does about the same amount of writing.)

When they have finished, explain that in the next session they will write the final part of this story.

4

IN THE END...

Teaching content
Rereading to get into the story; moving the plot forward; ending the story.

What you need
Robots, writing from the previous session, erasers, writing materials, paper smaller than A4.

What to do
Ask the children to work in the same pairs as before. Give the children a few minutes to read the story they have written together so far. Suggest that one partner in each pair reads the first half aloud and that the other partner reads the second half. Children should note any parts that are hard to understand, or words that are hard to read. Where appropriate, suggest they

rewrite these to make them clear. (Have plenty of erasers handy!)

Remind the children that in this session they are going to write the final part of their robot story. Give them a short while to discuss what could happen. Focus this discussion by asking what the robots do together. Do they:
• go somewhere?
• play something?
• find something or lose something?
• make or break something?
• see something happen?

Give the children a short while to discuss what their robots do and what happens to them in the end. When they have agreed, give each pair some paper and ask them to write the story in the same way as before, with each partner taking turns to write and advise on the writing. Suggest that the child who took the first turn at writing in the previous session should let the other partner begin this time.

At the end of the session, tell the children that they will be making their story into a book very soon. Suggest that they think about and discuss ideas for a good title before the next session.

Make sure that all the work for each story is collected together (there should be two robots, two written descriptions and two story parts per pair). You may want to mount the writing on sugar paper and/or A4 card before the next session, if the children are not going to do this themselves. If so, ask each pair to choose a colour (or colours) for their book and note this.

5

PUBLICATION!

♟ ⏱30

Teaching content

Presentation matters – the book must look good.

What you need

Work from all the previous sessions, art materials, A4 coloured card (or sugar paper as an alternative), sugar paper pre-cut for mounting work (if not mounted already), glue, paper, sticky tape, card for the front cover, craft materials such as sequins.

What to do

Tell the children that their story will be published as an A4 zigzag book. Each pair must decide on how they want their book to look. Explain that each pair will need six sheets of card or paper,

with one piece of work stuck on to each page: (1) picture of robot one (2) description of robot one (3) picture of robot two (4) description of robot two (5) what happens when the robots meet (6) the ending.

Tell the children that each piece of work will be mounted on paper to give it a border and then stuck on to the A4 sheets of card, which will form the page of the book. Each pair must choose:
• the colour of card or paper to use. Would they like to have the whole book in the same colour, to use alternate colours, or to use a whole variety?
• the colour of mounting paper to use (if the work has not been mounted already).

If the work is not mounted on a border, show the children how to do this carefully, leaving an even border all the way round.

Pasting the work on to the pages
Show the children how to 'centre' their work on the page, leaving an even border at the sides and at the bottom of the page, with a slightly larger space at the top. Explain that the sheets will eventually be joined together, so the children must take care to ensure that not only the work on each page is well-centred, but that it is

similar to that on the previous page. If all the sheets are laid out next to each other, the top of each piece of work should be in a straight line.

Joining the pages into a zigzag book
Ask the children to sequence their first two pieces of work (picture and description) and to tape the pieces of card together carefully. Show them how to line the card up, and to place sticky tape on the blank side so that it cannot be seen while reading the book. (Remind them to check that both pieces of work are the same way up.)

Now tell them to join these two pieces of work together, so that they have four pages in sequence, and then to add the penultimate and final pages one at a time. If you think that your class will find this very difficult, supervise them as they do it in small groups while the rest make their front cover.

Making the front cover
Give the children the paper for the front cover and remind them briefly of the details which they can expect to find on a front cover: the title, the author(s), and a picture relating to the story. Ask them to work in their pairs to design and make their cover. When this is finished, it should be glued on to the very front page of the book, on the other side of the picture of robot one.

CELEBRATION AND REVIEW

Teaching content
Celebration.

What you need
Books made by each pair, photocopiable page 94.

What to do
Put the children into groups of four. Explain that each pair will read their story to the others in their group. Show all the children a copy of photocopiable page 94 and explain that each writing pair will complete this after they have heard the story written by the other pair. Read through the sheet and explain each section. Make sure that the children understand that they may tick as many boxes as are applicable in the final section. Give the first pair an opportunity to show and read their book to the others in their group. Then, ask the second pair to do the same. Give out the photocopiable sheets (one per pair) for the children to complete. Encourage them to discuss this in their pairs and their groups, before choosing some children to share their stories/evaluations with the class.

Explain that four different books will be displayed in the library every two days. Thus, all the books will be available to the class, but on a rotation system. In this way, children can read all the books made by the class over the ensuing couple of weeks. Keep the children's interest alive over this period by regularly featuring the books at story time or 'together time'.

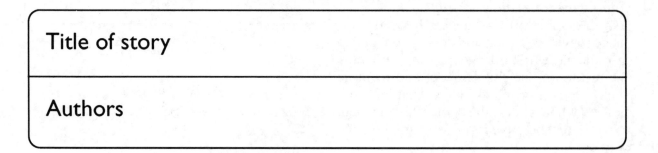

CELEBRATION AND REVIEW

Title of story	
Authors	

When we first saw the book, we thought:

   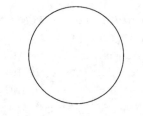

Yippee!
This will
be good

Will this
be good,
or not?

This will
need
careful
listening

(draw your own)

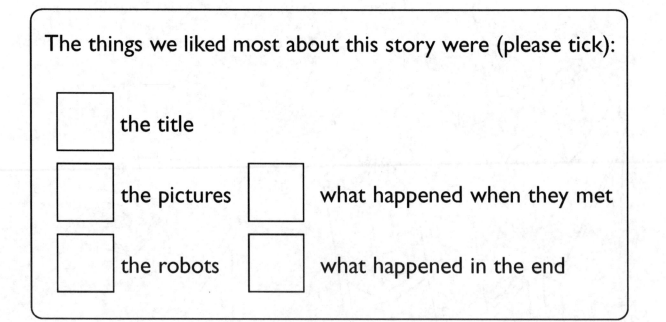

The things we liked most about this story were (please tick):

☐ the title

☐ the pictures   ☐ what happened when they met

☐ the robots   ☐ what happened in the end

Scholastic
WRITING
Workshop

Chapter Nine

THIS IS ME AND THIS IS WHAT I'M LIKE

INTRODUCTION

Project description

In this project children write two books about themselves. The first book is about the children as they are now ('This is me and this is what I'm like'). It is produced in class and provides a model for the second book about what the children were like when they were toddlers. This book is written in stages at home with the support of a parent or an older child.

Book 1. At the start of the project the children bring in photographs of themselves, or have them taken in class. These provide a focus for a short written description of themselves. Writing for this is supported by a word bank constructed with the class.

In the remaining sessions each child produces a series of short statements about what they like doing and why. Each statement is focused on a topic chosen by the teacher and introduced with a short class discussion. It is the teacher's decision as to how long the project should last and therefore how many pages the children produce.

Book 2 follows the same format as book 1 but is written/drawn by the children and their parents or other interested adults at home. The first topic is chosen by the teacher and introduced in class. The children take home a photocopiable sheet to complete with their parents and an explanatory letter.

Thereafter each new topic is introduced in class and discussed briefly with the children. At home, the children talk about this to their parents, asking for a memory or story about when they were small. Together, child and adult write/draw this on to the photocopiable sheet. As for book 1, the teacher decides how long the project should last.

Why this context?

Real life is an important source of ideas for storytellers and children find it interesting to write about themselves. Young children will be familiar with many commercial publications that build from real-life experiences. This familiarity with the structure and the content of the book is an excellent starting point for building confidence and enthusiasm for writing.

Through reading and discussing the books which they have written, young children can be encouraged to think about their own characters and characterisation in real life.

The project offers children support for writing in the form of a general starter sentence, which is similar for each new page, and a word bank. This allows children to write as much or as little as they wish, but leaves them free to decide on the specific content and structure. In this way children are offered support, but are also required to make more decisions in the composing process than would be possible were they to use a structure determined by a series of questions.

Finally, the importance of sharing the writing and story-making process with an adult who is close to the child cannot be underestimated. It encourages home–school links and provides a focus for parents to share writing with their children. The context ensures that each person in the parent–child partnership has something to offer: the child brings the experience and confidence of having made a similar book in the recent past and the parent is involved in generating and sharing ideas and not just in scribing for the child.

Project organisation

Children discuss their photographs in pairs at the start of the project. Thereafter they work as individuals. The writing demands are fairly straightforward and the project offers support in the form of a word bank and a starter sentence for each page.

Publication, celebration and review

The stories are published in an A5-sized book, which is made by folding A4 photocopiable sheets in half.

Book 1 is celebrated in class and at home. Book 2 is read to the class at 'together time' or story time, over a period of several weeks. The children witness their own books being read for enjoyment and are given an opportunity to expand on their stories.

An optional 'book launch' may also be planned, perhaps to coincide with a parent's evening or afternoon.

Books the children may find useful

Chatting (1994), *Bouncing* (1993), *Giving* (1993), *Hiding* (1994), all by Shirley Hughes, Walker Books

Things I Like, Antony Brown (1993) Walker Books

What I Like, Catherine & Laurence Anholt (1991) Walker Books

Ask the children to bring in a fairly recent photograph of themselves, or take photographs of the children in school, perhaps as they work in class, or in the playground at playtime.

1

INTRODUCING MYSELF

w →-ʈ‑ʈ (30)

Teaching content

Writing a character description: appearance, actions, preferences, personality.

What you need

A recent photograph of each child, A2/A3 paper or wordbank, photocopiable page 102, glue, writing materials, scissors (if required).

What to do

Tell the children to take a good look at the photograph they have in front of them. If they had to describe themselves to somebody else, what would they say? Give them a few minutes to think before asking a few children for brief comments. Encourage them to say what they look like, the kind of person they are and how this can be seen in the photograph.

Pick one child in the class and show him or her the photograph of someone who has not yet contributed to the discussion. What would he or she say about the person in this photo? Does the person agree?

Tell the children to show the person next to them their photograph and ask how this person would describe them. Is it similar to their own description of themselves? Did anyone get any surprises? What were they?

With the class, compile a word bank of key vocabulary used by the children during their discussions. Give each child a copy of photocopiable page 102. Tell the children to paste their photograph in the space provided under the words 'This is me'. It may be necessary to cut some of the photographs to size. Then ask the children to write a few sentences about themselves under the heading 'This is what I'm like. I like to...' Remind them to refer to the word bank for help while writing.

3

I LIKE TO HEAR STORIES READD BY...

✝ ㉕

Teaching content
Characterisation.

What you need
Chalkboard, photocopiable page 102, writing materials.

What to do
Talk to the children about their favourite stories and story books. When do they feel really content or happy listening to stories, and who reads them such stories? From the discussion, make a list on the board of all the people who read stories to the children.

Find out when and where their favourite story times take place: is it when they get up in the morning, go to sleep at night, when they come home from school, or when their parents come home from work? Ask the children to think hard and to each name one person who is really good at reading stories. What makes this person a good reader? Is it because of who they are; where they read the stories; because they put on good voices? Or maybe they act the story out, making it an exciting, scary or funny experience.

Give each child a copy of photocopiable page 102. Ask the children to draw themselves when they are being read a story by their favourite person on the top half of the sheet. On the lower half, ask them to complete the sentence 'This is what I'm like. I like to...' by adding 'hear stories read by...' before naming the storyteller and writing why this person's stories are so good.

2

THIS IS WHAT I LIKE

✝ ㉕

Teaching content
Characterisation through leisure activities.

What you need
Catalogues which include plenty of pictures of toys, photocopiable page 102, scissors, glue, writing and drawing materials.

What to do
Explain that everyone likes doing different things and playing with different things. Give the children the catalogues and ask them to imagine that they could choose any toy they like from them: it may be a favourite toy they already have at home; it may be a toy that they have only seen at a friend's house or on television. If their ideal toy is not in the catalogues, explain that they may draw it instead.

Tell the children to cut out their catalogue toy and paste this on to the top half of a copy of photocopiable page 102 under the heading 'This is me' and to draw themselves playing with the toy. On the lower half of the sheet, ask them to write about the toy which they have cut out by completing the sentence 'This is what I'm like. I like to...' They might add 'play with this toy because...' when they finish the sentence.

THE REST OF THE BOOK

✝ ⏲30

Teaching content

Characterisation; drawing on real-life experiences for a story.

What you need

A4 card folded in half, photocopiable page 102, stapler, glue, writing and drawing materials.

What to do

Run these sessions in exactly the same way as the previous ones in this project. Choose a focus for each session from the list below.
This is me and this is what I'm like. I like to:

- go to visit...
- talk to my friends about...
- laugh about...
- see my mum/dad/brother/sister doing...
- pretend I haven't noticed when...
- think about...
- make plans for...

Once the children have written the planned number of pages, show them how to paste the blank pages together after folding each A4 page in half (the writing is on the inside when the sheets are folded). Give the children folded sheets of A4 card and show them how to make a front and back cover for their book. They should choose a suitable title and ensure that this, along with the author and a suitable picture or design, is clearly displayed.

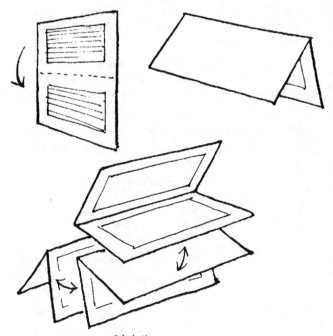

WE'RE ALL DIFFERENT

✝✝ ⏲25

Teaching content

Everyone has a different personality and character. This is shown by the different choices each person makes.

What you need

Books the children have made (book 1).

What to do

This activity is a celebration and review of book 1. When the children have finished their first book, put them into pairs and tell them to read and share their books with each other. You may need to give a demonstration to the children so that they understand exactly what is required. Do this by selecting two children from the class and asking them to read one book together. Then tell them to read the other book together. Ask the children what they liked about each book. Was there anything in either book that surprised them? Why?

Once the whole class have been given an opportunity to do this in pairs, select one or two pairs to read their books and talk about their ensuing discussion to the class. Encourage the children to reflect on the different ways in which people are individuals and how this individuality is shown.

Display all the books in the book corner of the classroom. Over the following few days, make a point of reading one or two books to the children at story time. See if the class can guess who wrote a particular book, simply from the description of the character.

THIS WAS ME AND THIS IS WHAT I WAS LIKE...

(W) (15)

Teaching content

Characterisation; writing with an important adult; using real-life experiences for stories.

What you need

A4 card folded in half, photocopiable pages 103 and 104, stapler, glue, writing and drawing materials, photograph of each child (optional).

What to do

Explain that the children are now going to make another book about themselves. However, they are not going to make this book in school, but at home and it will not be about themselves as they are now, but about themselves when they were small.

Show the children a copy of photocopiable page 103. Explain that this is similar to the ones completed for the 'This is me and this is what I'm like' book. Read briefly through the sheet and explore the possibilities of the topic you have chosen for today. Suggestions for suitable topics are listed in the next column.

This was me and this is what I was like. I liked to:
• dress in...
• go to sleep holding...
• cry when...
• make a mess when...
• play with...
• laugh about...
• go to visit...
• see people...
• eat when...

Explain that the children will need to take the sheet home and ask someone at home – a parent, older brother/sister or a grandparent – to tell them what they were like when they were small. (You may need to explain that although the children will undoubtedly remember some things, their parents will remember more!)

Tell the children to complete the copy of the photocopiable sheet with their parent. They should draw a picture (or paste a photograph) on the top half of the page to illustrate the story and write about it on the lower half. They can do all the drawing and writing themselves (asking the older person for help), share the drawing and writing with the older person (each taking turns), or ask the older person to scribe the story for them. If the latter option is chosen, the child must tell the older person exactly what to write.

Send home one page every couple of days, until enough pages to make the book have been completed. Each time a page has been completed, children should bring it back to school. This allows you to keep track of what each child is doing. An explanatory letter should accompany the first page home (see the example on photocopiable page 104, which you can photocopy on to headed notepaper or adapt to suit your needs).

Let the children begin to make their front cover in class, and then complete it at home. The front cover should be made from card as before, with the children choosing their own titles and design; of course, the authors of the book should be identified as both the child and the adult.

7

CELEBRATION AND REVIEW

Ⓦ ◯

Teaching content

Everyone has a different personality and character, shown by the different choices they make. Characters can change over time. Sharing writing with others is fun and can be done in different ways.

What you need

Books the children have made (books 1 and 2).

What to do

Once both books have been finished, display them in their pairs in the book corner with notices encouraging children to read each other's books and to think about how they have changed as people.

Over the next few weeks, make a point of selecting one or two books to read to the class at story time. Encourage the authors to talk about their different characters, about how they have developed and changed, and about the different ways in which they worked with the adults at home to draw and write their books.

THIS IS ME

This is me

This is what I'm like. I like to...

THIS WAS ME

This was me

This is what I was like. I liked to...

A LETTER HOME

The letter you send home to parents may want to explain all, or some, of the points made in the following letter.

Dear parent/ guardian,

For the past few weeks in school, your child has been involved in writing a book called 'This is me and this is what I'm like'.

The children are now working on writing books about what they were like when they were smaller, before they came to school. We would appreciate your help with this.

For the next few days, your child will bring home a series of photocopied sheets with a starter sentence on them for you and your child to talk and write about. Could you please complete these sheets with your child at home? Children have been asked to bring each completed sheet to class the following day.

Each sheet provides a space for a drawing or photograph and for some writing. You may help your child in any way you choose. There is no need to stick to one way of helping. In the past, parents have found the following ways successful:
• Write for your child, but let him or her tell you what to say;
• Write the sentence(s) on to a piece of scrap paper and let your child copy–write on to the photocopiable sheet;
• Share the writing by taking turns with your child to write directly onto the photocopiable sheet;
• Help your child to write directly on to the photocopiable sheet.

Of course you may help your child in similar ways with the drawing.

Please write clearly, in lower case, and make sure that, once finished, you read the writing through with your child.

I appreciate that you are busy and may not have a lot of spare time to spend on this with your child. If you are unable to do this, for any reason, it would be helpful if you could arrange for someone else – perhaps a grandparent, older brother or sister, or a close friend or neighbour – to help your child.

Please try to make this a relaxed, shared activity. You will help your child most by making this an enjoyable, fun and interesting experience.

Many thanks for your help.

Yours sincerely,

Scholastic
WRITING
Workshop

Chapter Ten

HOLIDAY SNAPS

INTRODUCTION

Project description

In this project children use personal photographs of a holiday or day out as a basis for writing individual stories. The central feature of the project is that children are writing a story based on an interesting incident in their own lives. The children talk to their parents about their recollections, look at family photographs and select their own photograph to bring to school.

In school the children talk about their photograph to a writing partner. Each child writes a three-part story. The story is structured by using a time sequence of the day which includes the child's morning thoughts, the incident in the photograph and their feelings at bedtime. The story is read to and commented on by the writing partner and by the adult who helped in the selection of the photograph.

Why this context?

Young and inexperienced writers often complain that they don't know what to write about in their stories. This project helps children to realise that their own lives can be a rich source of material for stories. Using a photograph of people and settings they know, and of an incident which they were closely involved in, provides the detailed content they need for their story. Talking about this with an adult at home acts as a rehearsal of the story. Sharing the photograph with a writing partner and answering their questions helps them to see the incident from the outside. This helps them to realise what has to be included in their writing so that a reader will understand their story. Using the time-sequence structure helps children to tell their story logically.

Children take their completed story home and share it with the adult who helped them to select the photograph. This joint involvement in the story at the beginning and at the end encourages heightened interest in the child's writing at home.

Project organisation

At the start of the project children, supported by adults at home, select a photograph of an interesting day out to use as the basis for their story. In pairs, supported by a photocopiable sheet of prompt questions, they help one another clarify and rehearse the details of the key characters, setting and events. Then individually they write a three-part story which sequences their day, from when they woke up on the day of the outing to the point when the photograph was taken and finally to when they went to bed that night. Again this is supported by a photocopiable sheet.

Publication, celebration and review

The story is published on A3 card folded into A4 to make a card with the folded edge on the left. On the front page the photograph is mounted centrally, with a suitable title above and the author's name below. The whole story (which is written on a photocopiable sheet) is pasted on the right-hand page inside the card.

When the story is complete it is shared firstly with the writing partner, who provides a positive written review which is then pasted on to the book cover. This review process provides positive feedback to the writer of how a reader of their own age responds to their story. Children then take their completed story home and ask the adult involved in the selection of the original photograph to write a short review. The involvement of an adult who is important to the child promotes interest in the child's story writing at home and affirms the child's identity as a story writer.

Books the children may find useful

A Day with Alice and Sam, 'The Street Fair', Sally Grindley (1993) Kingfisher
My Naughty Little Sister Story Book, Dorothy Edwards (1991) Methuen Children's Books
Our Puppy's Holiday, Ruth Brown (1987) Andersen Press

1

OTHER PEOPLE'S STORIES

Teaching content

Incidents in real life are a good starting point for stories.

What you need

A story book (see list on the opposite page).

What to do

Read the children a story about an incident in a child's life, preferably one featuring a holiday or an outing. (*My Naughty Little Sister* and the other suggested books provide examples of stories about real-life incidents.) Explain to the children that authors often use real people and real events to form the basis of their stories. Tell the children that they are going to write about something interesting which has happened in their own lives, but that they are going to write it and present it in the same way as an author would write a story.

Ask the children if they have photographs at home of a holiday or an outing that they have been on. This could have been with their family, friends, or a group or school. What is important is that they have a photograph of it and they know enough about it to discuss it in detail with a friend in school. Ask the children to go home and talk to their family about this, and to look through some photographs to find one which shows *one* interesting, enjoyable, funny or exciting thing that happened during their holiday or day out. Give the children and families time, preferably over a weekend, to select the photograph. Remind the children that their parents should agree that they can bring the photograph to school to write a story about it.

Talking over their recollections with their family will help children to remember and rehearse key events in their story. Ask the children to bring the photograph to school for the next writing session.

2

TELLING MY HOLIDAY STORY

Teaching content

Rehearsing the story by talking about the photograph will clarify key events and detail of characters and setting.

What you need

Children's holiday photographs (or photographs of an outing), photocopiable page 111.

What to do

Pair the children with a partner – someone with whom they would like to share their story. Tell the children that they will be taking it in turns to tell their partner about the photograph they have brought to school. Explain to the children that they have to describe to their partner what happened in their photograph. Tell the children who are the writing partners that if they are not clear about anything they have been told, or want to know more, they should ask questions to help them to find out the information.

Give each child a copy of photocopiable page 111, which they can use as a prompt sheet. Check that the children understand the prompt questions and explain that these are to help them to ensure that all the details their partner tells them are clearly explained. The boxes are to make notes of anything they want to remember for writing their story in the next writing session. Tell each pair which partner has to explain their photograph first and which has to ask the questions. After about ten minutes tell the children to swap roles.

At the end of the session, the photographs and prompt-sheet notes should be stored safely in the writer's file or in a folder. The notes are used as a reminder in the next session, but are not included in the final publication.

WRITING THE STORY

Teaching content
Sequencing the story over time. Using dialogue as an ending.

What you need
The children's holiday photographs (and a photograph of your own), photocopiable page 111 (completed in the previous session), photocopiable page 112 (A4 size, and enlarged to A3 size), writing materials.

What to do
Gather the children together with their photographs, and their notes that they made on a copy of photocopiable page 111 in the previous session, and explain that they are now going to write their story. Show the children an enlarged copy of photocopiable page 112 and a personal holiday photograph to use as an example with the class.

In the first box draw a picture of yourself waking up. Remind the children that this was the start of a special day, either a holiday or the day of an outing. Discuss with the children how they think you felt when you woke up that day and record some ideas.
• I was very excited because we were going to...
• I think the best part of the holiday will be...
Children can draw on these ideas or use their own, but it is useful to explore some possibilities.

For the second box refer to your own photograph and draw yourself either on holiday or on the outing. Encourage the children to help you describe the setting, place, physical detail and atmosphere, who was there, what happened and how it turned out by referring to the questions from the photocopiable sheet used in the previous session.

Remind the children that they have notes of their own answers to these questions on the prompt sheet which their partner completed, and that they have already thought about what to say about their own photograph.

In the final box draw a picture of yourself in bed that night and explain how you felt at the end of your special day and what you said to yourself that night when you curled up in bed. Explore with the children how some of them felt at the end of their special day and what they might have said to themselves. Remind the children that we would all feel different and say different things. Write on the sheet what you said to yourself, emphasising the key words or feelings in bold capitals or by some other means, for example:

Well! I hope **I N - E - V - E - R** have to go on a roller-coaster again!

Now give each child a copy of photocopiable page 112 and let the children draw and write their stories. Remind them that the story is in three parts and that they should:
• describe how they felt and what they did when they woke up on that special day;

- describe where they were in the photograph, who was with them and what happened;
- describe how they felt and what they said to themselves when they went to bed that night.

Tell them that they can look at your sheet to remind themselves how to complete theirs, but to refer to their own prompt sheet to make sure they use their own ideas. Remind the children that they can discuss their ideas on how to write the story with their writing partners.

When the sheets have been completed, store these in the writer's file or 'Holiday snaps' folder.

4

FINISHING OFF

Teaching content
Deciding on a title – the title should convey the essence of the story in a way which will engage a reader's attention and interest; putting all the pieces together for the publication.

What you need
Completed copies of photocopiable page 112, A3 card folded to make A4 card, writing materials (including scrap paper and broad felt-tipped pens).

What to do
Explain to the children that they will have to think of a good title for their story. Show them some titles from the books in this *Writing Workshop*, for example *Get Lost, Laura!* and *Mr Pam Pam and the Hullabazoo*. Discuss with the children how the title tells the reader something about the content or characters in a way that evokes interest and makes the reader want to read the story.

Tell the children that they must read their story carefully and decide what it was really about and what would be the most important part to highlight in the title. For example:
- They might wish to use their own name in the title because the story is their own.
- They might feel that the key incident in the story needs to have emphasis by being referred to in the title.
- Or perhaps the setting in which the event happened is the aspect of the story that they feel is important.

Remind them that the title should be quite short and that it must make someone interested enough in the story to want to read it.

Explain that they should try writing some possible titles on a piece of scrap paper. Then, when they are satisfied that they have two or three good titles, they should ask their writing partner to reread their story and choose which title they think best captures the story. They should mark this with a tick or a star to remind them which one the reader liked.

By now, the children will want to get their stories finished and published. Explain how to assemble their story by:
- pasting the completed copy of photocopiable page 112 inside the folded card;
- pasting the photograph in the middle of the front page;
- writing the selected title above the photograph in bold print;
- writing their own name underneath the photograph to indicate that they are the author.

CELEBRATION AND REVIEW

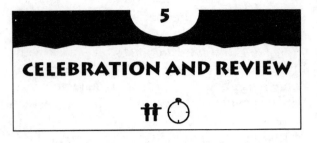

Teaching content

Writing a review by selecting something positive to say about a story.

What you need

Completed stories, slips of paper (cut to fit on the back of the story), glue, writing materials.

What to do

Tell the children that many books have comments on the back cover which say what people liked about the story. These are called reviews and they help other readers to decide whether to read the story. Explain that each child's writing partner and the adult at home who helped them choose the photograph are going to be asked to review the 'Holiday snaps' stories. Each reviewer will be asked to choose one thing they liked about the story.

Ask each child to read their writing partner's story and to decide which part they liked best. They should write this on a slip of paper and then write their name underneath.

When the review is ready, add quotation marks in bold black ink and the first review can be pasted on to the back of the book.

Let the children take their stories home at the end of the week and encourage them to share their story with the adult who helped them to select the photograph. Give the children a second slip of paper and ask them to explain to the adult how to write a brief review for the back of their book. They can use the writing partner's review, which has already been pasted on the book, as an example. Remind the children that the adult should pick out what they liked best about the story and write this on the slip of paper and add their name underneath. This should be put inside the story card and returned to the school. When the child brings the story back to school, add quotation marks to the comments that have been written. The children can then paste the second review on to the back of the story card. The finished stories can be displayed in the book area and children can be invited to read them and decide if they agree with the reviewers' comments.

After a week or so, the stories can be taken home and kept by the children's family.

TELLING MY HOLIDAY STORY

What was it like there?

Who was there?

What did people say or do?
What did you say or do?

What happened first?
What else happened?
What happened in the end?

How did you feel?

WRITING THE STORY

When I woke up in the morning I...

Then I...

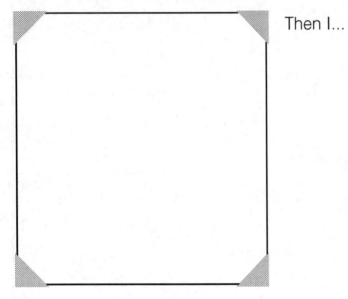

When I was lying in bed that night I said to myself, '...

Scholastic
WRITING
Workshop

Chapter Eleven

OUR HOUSE IS A VERY NICE HOUSE, BUT ONE DAY...

INTRODUCTION

Project description

In this project children role-play in a small group in the home corner. In the beginning the play is undirected and exploratory. This lets children try out roles and rehearse typical domestic incidents. In subsequent sessions the play is prompted by the introduction of resources which cause certain incidents or problems to arise. Each group has a different kind of incident: a birthday; the cooker is out of order; home decorating; a holiday; Granny coming on a visit; no water in the taps. The children are asked to tell stories about their play to the rest of the class and to record their stories in the form of a zigzag house-shaped book. In order to give children time to play, this project may last between two to three weeks. The actual writing can be completed over one week.

Why this context?

Young children are fascinated by and knowledgeable about a range of home settings, typical domestic incidents and the various roles of family members and visitors. In their role-play in the home corner children are encouraged to use this knowledge to create stories. This context helps children to recognise what they know and to use it in their story writing. Developing this as a play context provides children with opportunities to explore settings, describe characters and develop story-lines. Playing the story helps them rehearse their ideas. Telling their stories at report-back sessions and answering the questions of other children helps them to be clear about what the audience needs to know in order to understand the story. These are important 'drafting' processes for young and inexperienced writers.

When this was tried out with a class of six-year-olds the children were enthralled by each other's oral storytelling and wanted to hear group stories repeatedly. Writing the stories down and having them in the story corner means that the stories can be read again. Ensuring that the reason for writing the stories is clear and meaningful helps children to understand that writing is purposeful. Knowing who the audience is helps them to write with readers in mind.

Project organisation

Over two to three weeks, groups of children play together in the house. Each group has a set time to play and the chance to tell others in the class what has happened in their house play each day. The children are asked to write down the names of one or two special friends whom they would like to play with in the home corner. From this, the teacher can organise the class into groups of six. The same group plays together on each occasion. Each group has a set day to play in the home corner and tells their stories to the rest of the class at a later point that day. After the children have played freely in the house on one or two occasions, the teacher prompts story-lines in the play by introducing resources. As each group plays out and tells their prompted story, they can begin writing their house book. This ensures that one group is started off each day, which makes organisation easier. The children in the group are paired for the writing and each pair produces a book.

Publication, celebration and review

The story is published as a zigzag book, cut in the shape of a house. One book is required for each pair. The zigzag house-shaped book will help children to structure the sequence of their story and will form an attractive publication. Each pair reads their story to a pair in another group before placing their book in the story corner.

To make the book, an A1-size sheet of cartridge paper is folded in half with the fold at the top. It is then folded into quarters to make a zigzag A4 book. An outline of the roof is drawn on the front page. With the pages folded together, a roof outline is cut out to make each page house-shaped. Then a black marker pen is used to outline the roof and add slates to each page. The book has a front cover, four inside pages for writing and illustrating the story, and a back page for information about the authors. On the inside pages, midway between the roof and the bottom of the page, a thick black line is drawn to enable children to draw their illustrations above the line and then write their story below.

Books the children may find useful

All In One Piece, Jill Murphy (1991) Walker Books
An Evening at Alfie's, Shirley Hughes (1995) Red Fox
Doing The Washing, Sarah Garland (1995) Puffin

1

GETTING STARTED

♦♦♦♦ 🕐60

Teaching content

Play provides an opportunity for children to rehearse roles, characteristics, dialogue and to construct settings.

What you need

Home corner with table, chairs, cooker, sink and so on, dressing-up clothes, card for name-plate, chalkboard.

What to do

Before the children play, form them into groups of six, first asking them to write down the names of one or two special friends whom they would like to play with in the home corner.

Introduce the children in the group to each other and explain that over the next two to three weeks this group of children will play together in the house. Tell the children that each group will have a set day and time to play and will have the chance to tell others in the class what has happened in their house play each day.

Then ask each group of children to think of a name for their house. Children may need to be prompted to recall house names from their own street, from stories or from television. Talk to the children about how a house can have a name because it describes something about the house, for example 'Yew Tree Cottage' for the trees in the garden, or 'Hill House' or 'Station Cottage' for the house's location. Write each group's suggestions for a name on the board and help them to make a final decision. Then write each group's suggestion on their name-plate. Explain to the children that when it is their turn to play they should hang their house name on the door.

STATION HOUSE

Tell the groups, when it is their turn, that they can play whatever they want in the house but at a later point in the day the other children in the class will want to hear a story about what happened, for example in 'Daisy Cottage', that day.

You may wish to observe the children's play so that you can act as a prompt at the later storytelling session. You may also want to be on hand to help children to devise any resources or accessories that they need to support their play story. For younger children, or children not used to role-play in the classroom, you may need to be more involved in the children's play.

2

REHEARSAL – TELLING THE FREE-PLAY STORIES

Ⓦ 🕐10

Teaching content

Telling the story clarifies details of setting, characters and sequence of events. Answering questions clarifies the information the audience requires.

What you need

No resources needed.

What to do

At the reporting time you should try to establish a relaxed and informal atmosphere, perhaps in the story area. Select a pair of children from the group to be the main storytellers, but encourage the others in the group to provide additional details or to answer questions. (The pairs can be rotated in later sessions so that each pair has a turn to be the main storytellers.) Explain to the other children in the group that they should listen carefully to the story and ask questions about any part of the story which is not clear or they would like to know more about. When they have listened to the story, ask the storytellers and the audience to identify the parts of the play story they liked best.

If there is time, this activity should be repeated with different groups.

3

ONE DAY SOMETHING HAPPENED

Teaching content

Story-lines develop when something happens to change the usual routine.

What you need

In addition to the usual home-corner resources, one set of the following per group:

Group 1. Scenario – the cooker does not work.
A sign for the cooker which says 'Danger – out of order'

Group 2. Scenario – someone's birthday.
A child's birthday card posted through the door. Some party invitations in a box on the table. Some streamers, party bowls and bags.

Group 3. Scenario – the house needs decorating.
A cardboard box with two roller brushes and trays, four paint brushes and empty tins of paint, dust sheets, old shirts for overalls, some paint colour charts.

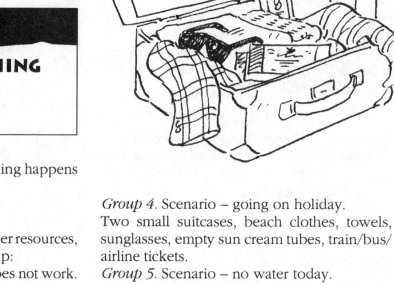

Group 4. Scenario – going on holiday.
Two small suitcases, beach clothes, towels, sunglasses, empty sun cream tubes, train/bus/airline tickets.

Group 5. Scenario – no water today.
A sign to hang on the taps which says 'No water today', buckets, basins, water carriers (for example, empty two-litre juice or milk containers), a set of plastic tools.

Group 6. Scenario – Granny is coming on a visit.
A letter posted through the door or delivered by the postman/woman. It is from Granny explaining that she is catching the 9 o'clock train/bus/flight and she will be arriving at lunchtime.

What to do

Before the children start to play, introduce one set of the resources to the house corner. Explain to the children that there is something different about the house today and that you think something unusual or exciting might happen in their play today. Assign to each group a different type of event or incident.

Encourage the children to use the resource as a starting point for their play. The play can go in many different directions and surprising story-lines may be created. For example, one group of children when faced with 'Danger – out of order' on their cooker speedily came to the conclusion that they would go to a café for their dinner. They dressed up, walked out of the door of the house, came back in and rearranged the furniture to be a café. They then took on roles as customers, cooks and waiters. Children in your class may have different ideas.

Observe the children but do not intervene unless children seem at a loss. It is useful if you can be on hand to help children to follow through their ideas. For example, in the birthday scenario children may want to write out party invitations, bake cakes and set out party food, decorate the house and devise party games. Your support may be necessary to develop resources or to help children to plan out what to do.

It is useful if you have an overview of the story-line the children develop so that you can prompt the telling or the writing of the stories by reminding them of key events.

4

TELLING THE 'ONE DAY SOMETHING HAPPENED' STORIES

𝍩𝍩 ⏱ 20

Teaching content

Writing stories down makes them permanent and they can be enjoyed again and again.

What you need

House-shaped book (see below).

What to do

First make a house-shaped book: fold an A1 sheet of cartridge paper in half with the fold at the top; fold into quarters to make an A4 zigzag book; draw an outline of the roof on the front page; cut out the roof outline with the pages folded together; using a black pen, outline the roof and draw slates on each page.

After each group has played out their story, invite them to share it with the rest of the class. When the children have said what they enjoyed about it, ask them if they would like to be able to share this story once more. Ask the children if they know what could be done with the story so that it could be read and enjoyed over and over again. Help the children to realise that by writing down the story it becomes permanent and can be read repeatedly. Show the house-shaped book to the class and explain that each pair will write a story about their play which will be published in the house-shaped book.

SETTING THE SCENE

♦♦♦♦→♦♦ ⏱20

Teaching content

The beginning of the story can be used to set the scene and introduce the characters.

What you need

House-shaped book made by folding an A1 sheet to make a zigzag and cutting out a roof outline – one book per pair (the top of each page should be decorated with roof-tile patterns; the inside pages should be divided in half by a bold black line), writing and drawing materials.

What to do

Explain that each pair is going to produce its own story book about their house-corner play. Tell the children that they are going to be story writers and story illustrators. Show the children *the first inside page* and explain that the top section of the page is to be used for drawing a picture of all the children in the group inside the house playing. Explain that they should draw each other 'being' whoever they were in the story and wearing the clothes they had dressed up in. Remind the children to put in as much detail as possible. Explain that the lower half of the page is for writing the story. Tell the children to describe who was in the house and what the house was like.

They should take it in turns to write, each writing a little and the other suggesting what to say and helping with the words. If necessary, supply starter sentences for beginner writers or help them to compose their stories using sentence makers (individual word cards of the words they would like to use).

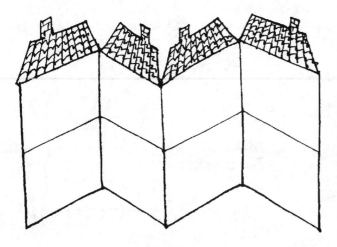

ONE DAY SOMETHING HAPPENED

♦♦♦♦→♦♦ ⏱30

Teaching content

A story plot requires a 'problem', event or incident. Using dialogue helps to convey mood and atmosphere.

What you need

Previously made house-shaped zigzag book with completed first page (on the second page at the top of the lower section are the words: 'One day when we came into the house...'), writing and drawing materials, photocopiable page 69 (optional).

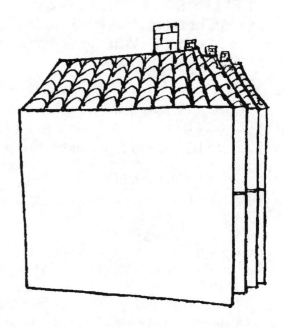

What to do

Remind the children of how they worked in the previous session, taking turns to draw and write. Show the children *the second page* of the zigzag book and explain to them that this is where they tell what happened in their story. Discuss with the children what it was that initiated their particular story. In the top section tell the children to draw what happened: this could be the cooker with the 'out of order' sign, or everyone listening to someone reading Granny's letter. In the lower section tell the children to complete the starter sentence to describe what happened and then to write down what everyone said. In addition, encourage children to select one or two phrases from their writing to be inserted in speech bubbles and placed on the illustration. (You could use speech bubbles copied and cut out from photocopiable page 69.)

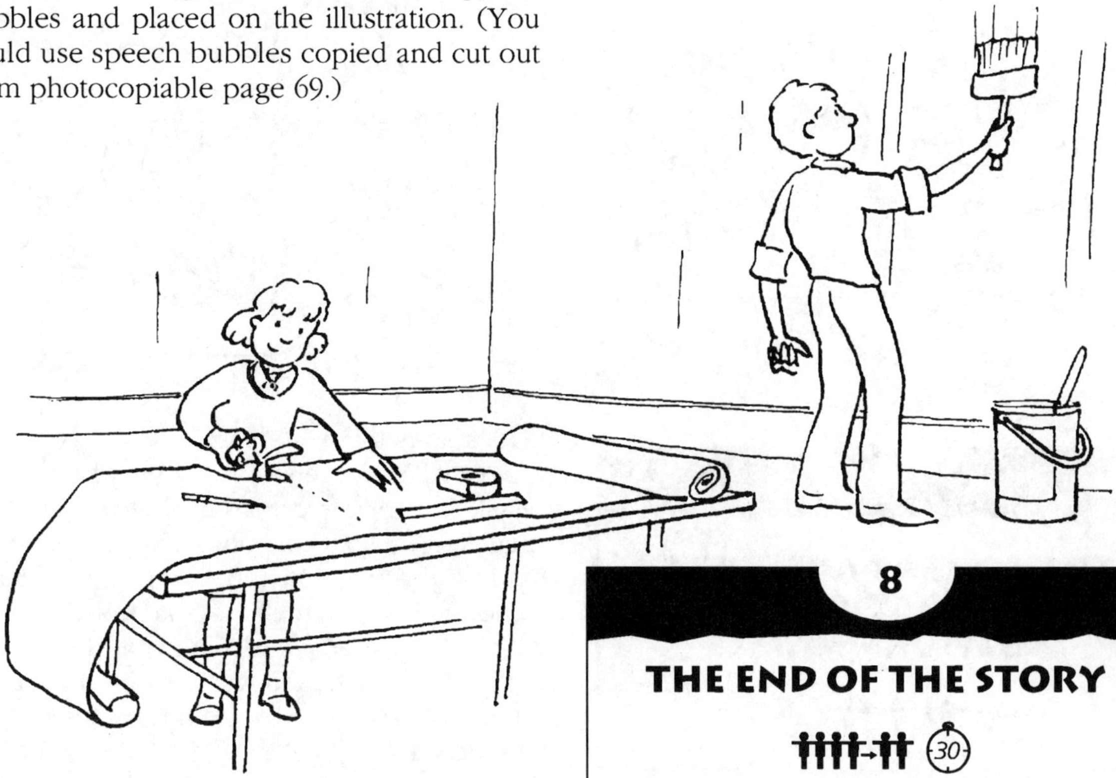

8

THE END OF THE STORY

⊬⊬⊬-⊬⊬ (30)

Teaching content
The end of a story should provide a conclusion which is satisfying to the reader.

What you need
House-shaped zigzag book (nearly completed), writing and drawing materials.

What to do
Explain to the children that they are going to write *the final page* of their story in this session. With each group explore what would make a suitable ending for their particular story. This might be how people felt at the end (Everyone was very happy to see Granny and they all cuddled her) or what they said and did ('That was a lovely meal,' said Mummy. 'Tomorrow we will go to the cooker shop and buy a new cooker.'), or what the house was like (The house was beautiful with its sparkling new paint).

Explore a number of possibilities with the children but remind them that they can write what they think will be a good ending for their story. Give the children time to think about this. Go round and talk to each pair and help them to decide on an appropriate ending. Again they should draw a picture and then write the story.

7

WHAT HAPPENED NEXT?

⊬⊬⊬-⊬⊬ (30)

Teaching content
Sequencing events.

What you need
House-shaped zigzag book from the previous session, writing and drawing materials.

What to do
Explain to the children that they are going to work together as they did before to write what happened next in their story. This might be getting dressed, going out to the café and having their meal, or moving the furniture, covering it with dust sheets and painting the walls. When the children have had the opportunity to remember these events, and have decided what they want to draw, they can complete *the third page* of their book by drawing the picture and writing the next part of the story.

9

THE COVER PAGE, TITLE, ILLUSTRATION AND AUTHORS' NAMES

††††-†† ⑳

Teaching content

Choosing a good title and illustration.

What you need

House-shaped zigzag book (story completed), scissors, glue, writing and drawing materials.

What to do

Explain to the children that they are now ready to make the front cover of their book and that this is very important as it is the cover that helps readers to notice a book and decide to read the story. Some front covers of story books could be discussed as examples (see suggested books on page 114). Talk about the illustrations and establish that front covers may have an illustration of a key part of the story or the main character. Now read the titles and explain that the title tells you something about the story in a way which invites the reader to open the book. Point out how titles are often quite short.

Tell the children to read through their completed story to decide what they would like to draw on the front cover and what title to give their story. Explain to the children that they should think about what their story was about and include this in the picture. This main aspect of the story should also be evident in the title. Remind the children that the title should tell the

reader something about the story in a way which will make them want to read on.

Ask each pair to reread their story and then suggest some possible titles. These should be noted on a piece of paper. When they have some suggestions, tell them to choose the one which they agree is best. The children can try writing this out in bold writing, before looking at their cover page and deciding how to position their title at the top of the page. They can write directly on the page or write the title on paper, cut out each word and position the words on the page, pasting them when they are satisfied with the layout. This will depend on the time available and the previous experience of the children.

Then ask the children to draw their illustration under the title, leaving enough space to add their names underneath. Suggest that they mark this section with pencil lines before printing their names.

10

ABOUT THE AUTHORS

††††-† ⑳

Teaching content

Authors are real people; children should recognise themselves as authors.

What you need

House-shaped zigzag book (finished and ready for the back cover to be done), photocopiable page 122 (including an enlarged A3-sized copy), scissors, glue, writing and drawing materials. Examples of books which have biographical details of the author on the back cover (optional). Passport-sized photograph of each child (optional).

What to do

Explain to the children that people are interested in knowing something about the authors who write stories. Sometimes a picture of the author and accompanying biographical details are on the back cover or jacket. If possible, show the children an example and read out what has been written about the author. Discuss with the children what kind of things are written. Establish that the writing may start with the author's full name and then say something about where the author lives, perhaps a bit about his or her family, and what he or she enjoys doing when they are not writing. It may also list other books which have been published by the same author. Show the children an enlarged copy of photocopiable page 122 and demonstrate how to write in the appropriate details.

Explain to the children that they are going to write biographical details for their house book so that people will know something about them as authors. Give each child a copy of photocopiable page 122 and tell them to think about the information which they would like to include about themselves in each section. When they have decided what they would like to include they should fill in the photocopiable sheet. Explain that they can draw a picture of their face in the box provided (like a passport photograph) or if they have a suitable photograph of themselves (cut to size, if necessary) they can paste it in the box.

When the children are satisfied with the details they have written, they should each cut out their biographical notes and paste them on the back page.

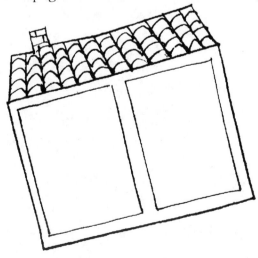

11

SHARING THE STORIES
ᛏᛏᛏᛏ (15)

Teaching content

Celebrating stories.

What you need

Completed house-shaped story books.

What to do

Make groups of four from two pairs and tell the children that they are going to read their stories to each other. Explain that each pair will take it in turns to read their story to the other pair as a celebration of their story. Ask the children to say what they like about the stories and the drawings. This has been an extended project for young children so an informal oral review will be more appropriate than asking the children to give a written review.

The children may want to have the opportunity to try out and play their own stories of all the different scenarios.

ABOUT THE AUTHORS

draw or stick your photo

my name →

my age →

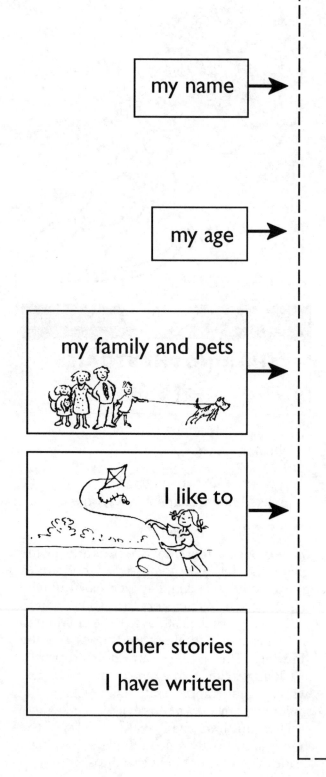

my family and pets →

I like to →

other stories
I have written

Scholastic
WRITING
Workshop

Chapter Twelve

NO PLACE LIKE HOME

INTRODUCTION

Project description

In this project half the class write a snowman's story and half write a hedgehog's story. Pairs of children begin by making a detailed setting either for the snowman, who needs to stay cold, or the winter hedgehog who needs to stay warm. Having completed their own character settings and descriptions, children visit a contrasting setting. The story develops from an imaginary visit by their own character, who has become bored with living in his own environment, to a character who lives in a very different setting. Their contrasting needs and preferences provide the 'problem' which the story hinges on.

Being able to visit and explore the settings provides the detailed knowledge which children will use in their writing. The completed boxes which show the settings of the stories and the unusual book in which the story is published are vivid and exciting, which helps to sustain the children's interest and gives them pride in their work. This is heightened by reviews completed by the children, working in the pairs in which they have been teamed throughout the story writing.

Why this context?

This context takes children into a make-believe world. This world is brought alive to the children by the concrete experience of creating an appropriate three-dimensional setting for their character, which helps children to build up a detailed knowledge of the setting for their story and of the character who inhabits it. A further concrete experience is provided by the opportunity to visit another setting physically, and experience it from the viewpoint of their own character. These experiences provide children with the knowledge they require to be confident about writing their story down. Creating the settings and characters helps the children to know the character in the way that only an author knows the characters and settings that he or she has created.

Project organisation

Before the project starts, the class is put into two groups, each group listening to a story. The stories provide the starter information required about each character. Pairs of children then create a setting for the character by using a box and craft materials. By doing this, the character becomes their own and they acquire a detailed knowledge of both the physical setting and their character's particular needs. Writing about this will help to fix details in their minds and will help the pair of children who 'visit' the home of the character later in the story writing. When the children examine a contrasting setting in detail, each pair adopts the viewpoint of their own character and explores their reactions to the visit and their feelings on returning home. This forms the key content of the story.

Publication, celebration and review

The book is published as a 'turning' book, with each page carrying one part of the story. Children work in pairs to illustrate and write a joint story. They then make the book and publish their story in it. Each pair is teamed with another pair who act as audience and reviewer. The books are then suspended at eye-level just above the three-dimensional settings to provide an impressive and inviting display.

Books the children may find useful

The Happy Hedgehog Band, Martin Waddell (1991) Walker Books

The Mixed Up Chameleon, Eric Carle (1988) Puffin

A House for A Hermit Crab, Eric Carle (1987) Hodder & Stoughton

For more experienced writers:

The Prince and the Firebird, Krystyna Turska (1982) Hodder & Stoughton

The Snow Queen, Hans Christian Andersen, adapted by Anthea Bell (1987) North South Books

Divide the children in the class into two groups. Read *The Snowman* by Raymond Briggs (Hamilton, 1978) to one group, and then *The Winter Hedgehog* by Ann Cartwright (Hutchinson, 1989) to the other group. You may wish to read other children's stories about snowmen or hedgehogs which are appropriate.

A SPECIAL ROOM

Teaching content

Creating a setting for a character will help children to 'own' and live with the characters and settings, helping to build up detailed knowledge of the setting and the character.

What you need

Cardboard boxes (apple boxes are about the right size), selection of junk materials (for example, egg cartons, tubes and boxes), sticky tape, glue, staplers, scissors, chalkboard/A2 paper.

Snowman resources – selection of cotton wool, white net, white and pale blue tissue or crêpe paper, silver sequins or glitter, silver paper, white wool.

Hedgehog resources – selection of orange and brown material, cloth or leather scraps, some dry leaves, nuts or small fir cones, twigs, brown and orange wool.

What to do

Group 1

Put the children into pairs. Remind the children of the snowman and how he needs to stay very cold all winter. Tell the children that they are going to make a room for the snowman to live in, but that it has to be a very cold room. Explain that each pair will have a box and inside the box they will make the snowman's room. Write the following questions on the board or on a large sheet of paper and discuss them with the children:

• What would the floor be like?

• What would the ceiling be like?
• What would the walls and windows be like?
• What kind of furniture would he have? Would there be a bed, chairs, table and so on?
• What kind of things would he like to do to relax?
• What kind of things would he like to eat?

Show the children the snowman resources and discuss how these could be used. Give out the large boxes, one to each pair, and explain to the children that they should first spend a few minutes thinking about the walls, the ceiling and the floor of their character's room. What would these need to be like in order for the snowman to keep cold? Tell the children to make these first before deciding on the furniture and other details. The egg cartons, tubes and boxes can be cut up to make the furniture. These can then be covered in the kinds of materials which would keep the snowman cold. Remind the children to refer to the questions, which you have written down, to help them to think about all the details they need to include. When the room is finished, tell the children to cover the roof in 'snow' material.

Group 2

Remind the children about the hedgehog and how he was looking for a home to stay warm and cosy in all winter. Then follow the procedures for making the snowman's room, but use the hedgehog resources. Discuss what would be needed in the room in order to keep the hedgehog warm.

WRITING THE DESCRIPTION
††⏱20

Teaching content

The setting is appropriate for the character's lifestyle. Describing this in detail helps to reinforce the character's needs and likes and how these are catered for in the setting.

What you need

The children's characters' rooms, card, questions from the previous session (written on the board or on paper), camera (optional).

What to do

This activity should be carried out as soon as possible after the completion of the characters' rooms – the same afternoon if there is time.

Tell the children to work in their original pairs. Give each pair a piece of card. Explain that they are going to write a description of the room they have made. At the top of their card they should write either 'The snowman's room' or 'The hedgehog's room'.

Give the children the appropriate starter sentence.

The snowman wanted a room where he could stay cold all winter. It...
The hedgehog wanted a warm and cosy room for the winter. It...

Explain to the children that they have to describe exactly what their room is like and why it needs to be cold or warm. Remind them to look carefully at all the details in the room they have made and describe these. Tell them that they can refer to the prompt questions on the board (or on the sheet of paper) to help them to sequence their description, starting with the descriptions of the floor, walls and ceiling and then moving on to the other details. One child can write and the other child can help by suggesting what to say and which words would be appropriate to use. The children should take turns to be the writer and the supporter. For instance, they could either take turns to write the answer to the questions or one child could write about the floor, walls and ceiling and the other child could write about the details.

When they have finished, they should display the completed room and description card together on a suitable table or shelf. Give the children time to look round all the completed rooms and to read the descriptions.

If possible, photograph the interior of each box so that you can use the photographs on the covers of the books.

3

A BORING LIFE
††⏱20

Teaching content

Using the character's thoughts or speech to identify a problem.

What you need

Completed boxes, photocopiable page 31, blank A4 paper, chalkboard, scissors.

What to do

Explain to the children that now their rooms are completed they are going to write a story about their character. Explain that, although the snowman likes his nice cold room very much, sometimes he gets bored and wants something different, and that although the hedgehog loves to curl up in a nice cosy den sometimes he wants to do something more exciting. Tell the children that for these reasons the snowman and the hedgehog decide to visit each other.

Ask each pair to think about their character and to decide what the character might be bored with and what he might think or say to himself one day when he is bored. When the children have had a few minutes to think about this and discuss it, take one suggestion from each pair. If you think children need some support note the suggestions on the board.

Give each pair of children an A4 piece of paper. (Remind them to keep it vertical so it will fit correctly on the book. Remember this at each session.) Explain that they are to draw a picture of their character at home looking bored.

Next give each pair a speech bubble cut out from a copy of photocopiable page 31 and tell them that you would like them to write what the snowman or the hedgehog says to himself which shows that he is bored.

When the children have completed their drawings, ask them to paste on the speech bubble. When the page is dry, children should keep it in their writer's folder or in a file for this project.

4

VISITING

👥 ⏱30

Teaching content

Characters have different viewpoints, reactions and preferences.

What you need

Completed boxes, A4 paper, chalkboard, writing and drawing materials.

What to do

Gather all the children together. Then allocate each snowman pair to a hedgehog pair. These pairs will exchange visits and be the audience for one another's writing at the end.

Tell the pairs that their character is going on a visit to another house. Explain that they must look very closely at the other room, read the description and decide how their character would feel when he first saw the other character's house. Remind the children that the snowman and the hedgehog were bored with their own homes and wanted something different and exciting.

Write the following questions on the board and ask the children to think about them carefully. Explain that the questions will help them to see the other house from their character's point of view.

What would the snowman notice about the hedgehog's house? It might be something: belonging to the hedgehog; on the walls; about the furniture; scattered around the floor; or something else.
The snowman immediately likes one thing about the hedgehog's house! What is it?

What would the hedgehog notice about the snowman's house? It might be something: belonging to the snowman; on the walls; about the furniture; scattered around the floor; or something else.
The hedgehog immediately likes one thing about the snowman's house! What is it?

Give each pair a blank sheet of A4 paper and explain that on the top half of the page they should draw what the snowman or the hedgehog saw. Underneath they should explain how their character reacted to the house. Remind the children to think about the questions on the board.

Tell the children to take it in turns to write and draw. When they have finished, the completed pages should be stored in a folder.

5

A CONVERSATION
👥 ⏱30

Teaching content

Characters react differently. Writers can show this through what characters say. Illustrators can show this through facial expressions. How characters react to one another can provide turning points in a story.

What you need

Photocopiable pages 132 to 134, writing and drawing materials.

What to do

Split the class into the snowman story group and the hedgehog story group. Work with the snowman group first and then repeat the session with the hedgehog group.

Put the children in their original pairs. Tell the pairs to think about their character and remember that they made the snowman's home especially for this snowman, to suit what he needed and what he liked. Give the children a few minutes to revisit the home they made and to think about the kinds of things the snowman liked and needed.

Then gather the children together and tell them that during the snowman's visit to the hedgehog, they decided to have tea. Show the children photocopiable page 132 and explain that this shows the conversation between the hedgehog and the snowman. What the hedgehog said is included but not how the snowman replied. Tell the children to look at the first thing the hedgehog said. Tell them to remember what their snowman was like and decide what he would say. Then do the same for the other speech bubbles. Now tell the children to write down what they think the snowman would say.

When they have finished, ask them to read through their completed conversations. Ask them how they think their snowman would be feeling. Explain to the children that they are going to draw in the expression on their snowman's face to show how he is feeling at the end of the conversation, but first of all they are going to practise how to do this.

Now show them the snowman half of photocopiable page 134. It shows a variety of different facial expressions (surprised, worried, happy, unhappy) and how these have been created by changing the shape and position of eyebrows, eyes and mouths. Help the children to identify the different kinds of expressions and how these have been drawn. Underneath are a row of blank faces where children can try out these different effects.

When children have had some practice, tell them to reread the conversation and to remember how the snowman felt. Then they can draw in the expression on the blank face of the snowman on photocopiable page 132. Store the completed sheet in a file or folder.

Repeat the session with the hedgehog group using photocopiable page 133 and substituting the hedgehog's replies and feelings for the snowman's. Let the children practise hedgehog expressions on the hedgehog half of page 134. Then tell them to complete the expression on the face of their hedgehog. Store the completed sheet in a file or folder.

WHAT HAPPENS IN THE END?

†† ⏱20

Teaching content

The ending has to resolve the events in the story in a way that is satisfactory to the reader.

What you need

Writing and drawing materials (including A4 paper), completed writing from the previous session, photocopiable page 31.

What to do

Gather the children together and ask them to reread their conversation between the hedgehog and the snowman. The final question is, 'Would you like to stay the night?' Each pair may have a different answer. Tell the children that they need to decide what happened next and how the story ended. Give each pair some time to discuss what they think their character would do and how he would feel. If the children need support in finding a suitable ending, you might want to explore some possibilities with the children. For example:

If he stayed the night –
• Did he enjoy it and want to stay longer?
• Did he want to leave and go home?
• How does he feel now?

If he turned down the invitation to stay the night –
• What did he do?
• Where did he go?
• How does he feel now about the visit?

Give each pair a sheet of A4 paper. Tell the children to decide how the story ended and to draw a picture showing what their character is doing and how he might be feeling. This might be back at home:
• sitting in a favourite chair;
• eating favourite food;
• resting in bed.

Or it might be something else. The children must decide. Tell them to write at the bottom of the page what their character thought of his friend's house and how he feels now.

Give each pair a speech bubble cut out from a copy of photocopiable page 31 and ask them what they think their character would be saying to himself. Tell them to write this in the speech bubble and then paste it on to their drawing.

Remind the children to take it in turns to write and draw. Store the completed pages in a file or folder.

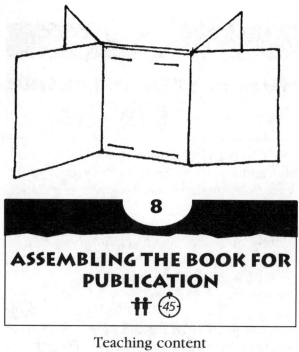

7

BOOK CONSTRUCTION

†† (30)

Teaching content
Book construction.

What you need
A3 sugar paper, glue.

What to do
This is quite a complicated procedure so it may be best to try it out first so that you have a model of the completed book. When teaching the children, go through the instructions one by one and check that each pair has managed to follow them.

Give each pair of children two sheets of A3 paper. Tell one child to fold one sheet in half with the folded edge on the left-hand side, then to cover the side which is facing up with paste. Tell the other child to fold their A3 sheet in half with the folded edge on the left-hand side, then to stick it on top of their partner's folded sheet. Ensure that it is firmly pressed down.

Give each pair another two A3 sheets and repeat the above procedures. Tell each pair to open up their book and stand it with the pasted sheets facing the middle and the other sheets like wings at the side. One child should have the paper positioned with the wings to the left side and the other child with the wings to the right side.

Tell the children to put the pasted pages together and to hold them in the middle. They should now see how the book will look and can staple the pasted centre pages together, with the middle section together and the two wings at either side. The completed book forms a central panel with the two wings at each side.

Children can lightly pencil their names on one side and then they can be put aside to dry.

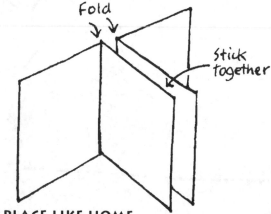

Fold

Stick together

8

ASSEMBLING THE BOOK FOR PUBLICATION

†† (45)

Teaching content
Choosing a title, finishing the book for publication.

What you need
Photographs of completed boxes, scrap paper, broad felt-tipped pens, hole punch, cord.

What to do
Discuss with the children possible titles for their story. Remind them that the title imparts something about the content or characters in a way which interests the reader and makes him or her want to read the story.

Ask the children to take the four pages of their story out of their folders and lay them out in order. Tell them that they must read their story carefully, think about the content and decide what would be the most important part to highlight in the title. Tell them to write some suggestions for their title on scrap paper and then choose the one which they think best conveys what they want to say about their story.

When the books are dry, tell each pair to take their book and to lay it out flat on the table. The children should write their chosen title at the top of one side of the centre panel. Underneath they should paste the photograph of their box. At the bottom they should write their names. Leave aside for a few minutes to dry.

Then tell the children to stand their book up with the two wings facing them and the title in the middle facing right. Tell one child to put paste on the back of the first sheet of their story. The other child should put paste on the back of the second sheet. The first child then pastes the first page on the left-hand wing of the book.

The second child should paste the second page on the right-hand wing of the book.

When both pages have been pasted on, the whole book should be turned round, with the title now facing the left-hand side. Go through the same procedures to paste the third page of the story to the left-hand wing and the last page to the right-hand wing.

Punch a hole at the centre top of the title page and attach the cord ready to suspend the book above the box houses.

These last two sessions could be combined if you have sufficient time and you think children could concentrate on it for longer.

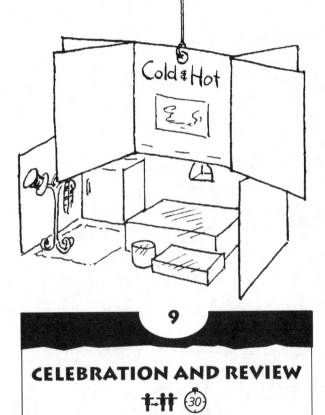

9

CELEBRATION AND REVIEW
†-†† ⏱30

Teaching content
Reviewing a book to persuade others to read it.

What you need
The children's completed stories, writing materials.

What to do
Explain to the children that they are going to review the story which has been written by the children who have visited their character's house. Ask them to read the story and decide on three things which they liked about it. This could be:

• the drawing of the character they liked best and why they liked it;

• the way the story began or ended and what they liked about it;

• the way the book was presented.

Give the children time to read the completed books and note their ideas on scrap paper. Match each pair up and give them time to discuss what they liked about each other's books.

Gather all the children together and explain that publishers often put comments from reviewers on the back covers of books which point out what readers might like about the story. You could read some examples from a favourite book. Explain that the children are going to be the reviewers of each other's stories and that their comments and their names will be pasted on the back of the completed book.

Write some review starters on a large sheet of paper, for example:

• A treat, don't miss the...
• You'll love the...
• Schoolchildren will especially enjoy...
• The best bit of this book...
• Look out for...

Discuss with the children how they could use these with the notes they have already made to produce review comments.

Children should produce several reviews, write them in their best handwriting on slips of paper and sign them underneath. Then each pair should team up with the pair whose story they were reviewing. The authors should choose the two reviews they think would be best for persuading other readers to read their stories. They should paste these on to the remaining blank face of the book. The completed books can then be suspended above the 'box rooms' to enable others to read them. If they cannot be suspended, an alternative would be to place the box and the book side by side on a table or worktop area.

THE HEDGEHOG'S CONVERSATION

Do have some more warm berry juice and some toasted nuts.

Is it getting cold in here?
Shall I put another log on the fire?

Would you like to stay the night?

THE SNOWMAN'S CONVERSATION

Would you like some more
iced tea or a snowball cake?

Is it getting hot in here?
Shall I open the window?

Would you like to stay the night?

EXPRESSIONS

surprised worried happy unhappy

surprised worried happy unhappy

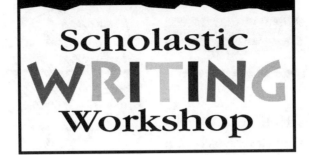

Chapter Thirteen

BIG BOX DENS

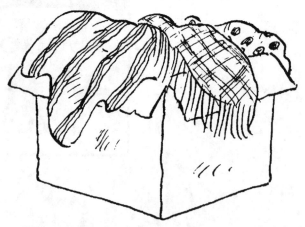

INTRODUCTION

Project description

'Big Box Dens' is an open imaginative context through which children create play and story settings, develop characterisation and story-lines. It begins with children playing with a big box, drapes and other resources to create a place to play in. The type of place created is of the children's choosing, although sometimes the teacher may encourage the children in certain directions by the choice of resources.

This project is designed for very young writers, and the writing is confined to the children describing the place that they have created and what they did there. The presentation in the form of a card with a bordered title page and an inner page with a lift-up flap enables the teacher to introduce presentation ideas which the children may use in later stories. The care and attention given to the presentation and publication will enhance children's assessment of their own writing and of themselves as writers.

Why this context?

This context allows children to be imaginative and creative by developing the settings, characters and stories which they are really interested in. Having the concrete experience of creating the settings and then using them helps children to build up detailed knowledge of settings, characters and of the types of stories which different settings evoke. The children have to co-operate and come to joint decisions. This is important for helping them to share their ideas.

Talking about their ideas and explaining them to one another helps them to clarify which details need to be explained and how best to do this. This is similar to thinking about what a reader needs to know. Even minor disagreements can be useful in adding detail, either because children have to justify what they want or because compromises can extend settings and stories. For example, two boys argue about what to do with some boxes:

'Let's make it a train.'

'No! Let's make it a carnival float.'

The argument goes back and forth for a few minutes until one child says, 'Let's make it a train going to a carnival!'

Being given the opportunity to record their play as stories focuses children's attention on how writing can be used as a way of preserving stories and as a means of sharing ideas with other writers.

Project organisation

The context begins with free play in groups of four. Children work together to decide on settings, and characters and actions. When the play is finished, the children record the place they made and describe what they did in it. They then illustrate their story with a bordered title page and a flap-up box to add interest. The stories are shared with other children within the class, before being displayed.

Publication, celebration and review

The story is published as a simple two-part card story. The inner page has a box lid lift-up flap which conceals the illustration of the place created. The second page has a simple written description of the place which was created and of what happened. The title page has an attractive border which picks up details of the story. The author's name is prominent to reinforce children's feeling of authorship. Children read their stories to a group of children who have not been involved in the same playing group. Finally, all of the stories are placed in a decorative box, which is placed in the story corner where children can access them when they want to reread them.

Books the children may find useful

Whatever Next?, Jill Murphy (1983) Macmillan
Sari Games, Naina Gandhi (1990) André Deutsch
Alice's Blue Cloth, Deborah vander Beck (1988) Picadilly
My Book of Nursery Rhymes, Caroline Crossley (1992)
Safeway Starter Books (for examples of border pages)

1

BIG BOX PLAY

Teaching content
Creating settings and playing out appropriate story-lines and roles. Writing down stories helps us to share them with others.

What you need
A big box (washing-machine size or similar), a box containing a selection of different-coloured drapes (old curtains and remnants), netting, cushions, soft toys, other appropriate role-play accessories.

What to do
Set up the resources in an appropriate space where children can play without too much disturbance. The resources can be selected randomly or with certain topics in mind. For example, a seashore topic might include blue and green silky or transparent material, yellow, green and brown drapes, a length of fine fishing net, access to picnic sets or swimming rings, goggles and towels, or paddles and fishing rods. Soft toys can often be included to share the adventure. Children may create beach caves, boats or beach huts, something imaginative like an undersea world or something totally disconnected to the seashore. Having freedom to use their own imagination is crucial.

Explain to the children whose turn it is to play that they can play in the big-box area for about half-an-hour and that they can use the material and the box to make up whatever kind of place they want. When they have made their place they can play in it. Remind the children not to be too rowdy and not to spill out into other areas where other children are busy. Tell the children where they can collect dressing-up clothes or other accessories if they think these are needed.

Explain to them that the box will be in the classroom for about a week and that all the children will have a chance to play. Tell the children that others would be interested in the stories they tell when they are playing, so this week, at the end of the playing time, there will be some time for writing and drawing the stories they have played. Then at the end of the week there will be a story-sharing session so that all of the children can find out about all the

play places and stories. Remind the children to pack all the materials away at tidy-up time.

Let the children play undisturbed, but keep an eye on what is happening so that you have an idea of the content of their play, the settings, characters and story-lines created. It is interesting to observe how or if children draw on the experience of stories they have read to develop their play.

2

MY BIG BOX STORY

Teaching content
Describing setting and actions.

What you need
A3 page folded in half, then folded in half again to make a card, with a lift-up flap cut into the inner left-hand page. (The cover page should have a border of about 4cm marked with a bold black line. In the centre of the box write 'My big box story' and underneath 'by', providing a space for the author's name – see 'Further development' in the next activity 'Title page'.) Writing and drawing materials.

What to do
Give each child his or her card and point out the flap on the inside page. Explain to the children that this is like the box they were playing with. Tell the children to think about the place they made, the story they played and what they thought was the best part of their play story. Ask them to lift the lid of the box and draw a picture of the place they made and of what they did there. On the facing page they should write a story which describes the place

and what they did. Even the youngest writers should be encouraged to write. Give support by helping them with difficult words, or by writing 'This is the place we made for the story' and 'This was the best bit of the play story'. The children could draw a picture for each sentence and label it. Your knowledge of individual children will help you to judge which is the best approach for each writer.

When the children have completed their writing and drawing, explain that they must colour in their box lid so that it stands out from the page. Either a solid block of colour, stripes, or a clear outline with a pattern inside would be best. When the children have finished their colouring, they should write in black across the flap: 'Open the box'.

You can pencil their initials lightly on the back, and then keep the completed cards in the children's writing folders until the next session.

TITLE PAGE

Teaching content

Stories have titles. Authors' names appear on the title page. Presentation can be enhanced by borders. Border design can give clues to the story.

What you need

Completed story cards, chalkboard, writing and drawing materials.

What to do

Explain to the children that you have written the title of the story on the page but that they must write their own names underneath as they are the authors.

Point to the border and explain that the children are going to decorate their title page with a colourful border. Tell the children that borders can sometimes be made with zigzags, stripes or lines, but for this story they are going to think about the place they made, and what they played, and draw small pictures of items connected with the place or their play round the edge of the page. So if they made a boat and sailed away, they could draw small boats and waves as a border. If the children have not done this before, show them some examples or demonstrate how to draw an appropriate border

on the board. Let the children discuss their ideas with you before they start drawing.

Further development

If there is time and you judge it to be appropriate, the children could devise their own titles. It would be best to do this after the border making. Other projects in this *Writing Workshop* give advice about how to teach children about selecting a good title. The completed cards should be kept in the children's writing folders until the next session.

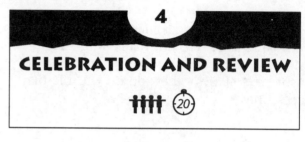

CELEBRATION AND REVIEW

Teaching Content

Authors write different stories. Presenting their stories will help children to build up their identity as an author.

What you need

Completed story cards, decorated box with the words 'Open the box' on the lid.

What to do

When all the children have written their stories, put them into different groups from the playing groups and try to have a variety of story settings and stories represented in each group. Explain that each child must take it in turn to read their story to the group and show the border and flap-up picture. The other children in the group can ask questions about the story or about the illustration or borders.

When the stories have been read, show the children the decorated box and ask them to put their stories inside. Place the box in the story corner to enable the children to read the stories as often as they wish.

Chapter Fourteen

MEET MY MONSTER

INTRODUCTION

Project description

In this project children start by creating an imaginative monster character. Each child creates his or her own monster and own individual story. The story is built around a series of meetings and reactions when the monster decides to go to school. Making the monster character and moving it from page to page throughout the book sustains the children's interest. To conclude the activity, children are paired with an older child who will evaluate the final story.

Why this context?

Young children are fascinated by monster stories. This context enables them to create a detailed and believable monster with personality and personal tastes. Although the character is imaginary, children can draw on their previous knowledge of pets, and also on their detailed knowledge of school settings and people they know, to create a rounded character. This helps children to be confident in their writing. Encouraging the writers to view people they know well as potential characters for the story enables them to understand that authors may make use of some of the characteristics of real people in imaginary stories.

There is a comic element in this story. Children imagine their close friends and their teacher confronting the monster, and then the runaway monster bumping into the headteacher. This should add to their enjoyment of the story and sustain their interest. The 'big book' format and moveable monster character resembles published books, which helps the children to feel like real authors.

Project organisation

This project could be undertaken by the whole class or by one group from within the class depending on numbers, time and resources. The project begins with the creation of the identikit monster and then the addition of other physical details. However, from the beginning, the children are encouraged to think of their character in a more rounded way by exploring its personality, behaviour and tastes. Naming the character and introducing it to others helps children to rehearse and internalise all of these details. The children are then presented with a problem: their pet monster goes to school. The story takes off from there and is sequenced by introducing various people for the monster to meet. Their reactions carry the story forward. Then the children are guided to a satisfying conclusion by considering how the monster would feel. The writer, by taking on the role of rescuer, can control the ending and round off the story. Having older children evaluate the story should increase the children's confidence in themselves as story writers.

Publication, celebration and review

The story is published in a 'big book' format made from A3 sugar paper. The pages are assembled session by session (placed landscape) and finally stapled together to make the book. The use of Velcro strips enables the monster to be moved from page to page, saving a lot of drawing as well as maintaining interest. The use of illustrations of people who are well known to the children should enrich the illustrations as well as informing the writing. The finished books should be impressive and worthy of scrutiny by older pupils. Briefing the older pupils first and structuring their evaluations positively should encourage the young writers.

Books the children may find useful

These should be read after the children have completed their own monster story. This will help them to read the published monster stories with an author's eye.

The Last Noo-Noo, Jill Murphy (1995) Walker Books

Monster Monday, Susanna Gretz (1994) (BBC Books)

I Was a Class 2 Werewolf, Daniel Pinkwater (1983) Picturemac

MAKING MY MONSTER

W→✝ 45

Teaching content
Creating detail of character appearance and personality.

What you need
Photocopiable pages 147 and 148, wool, scraps of cloth, plastic, leather, feathers, fake-fur oddments, pieces of knitting, drawing materials (including fluorescent felt-tipped pens), glue, poster of prompt questions (see below).

What to do
Gather the children together. Ask the children about the pets they have:
- What do you like about your pet?
- What does your pet like to do?
- How does your pet behave when it is happy?
- What annoys your pet?
- How does your pet behave when it is annoyed?
- What does your pet like to eat?
- Where does your pet like to sleep?

Now explain to the children that they are each going to have a special classroom pet, a monster pet. Everyone will make one and then write stories about their monster pet coming to school. Show the children a copy of photocopiable page 147 and explain about the proportion of the monster and where its head, body, legs, feet and tail should be positioned. Explain that every child will make their own pet monster. Give each child a copy of photocopiable page 148 which has different heads, bodies, legs, feet and tails. Explain that the children can choose any combination, for example pointy horns, a hairy body and a spiky tail, and that they should cut and paste them on to the spaces on the blank photocopiable sheet to make a complete pet monster. Now show them the selection of resources and explain that they can make their monster spotty or stripy (using fluorescent felt-tipped pens), furry, hairy or woolly, or smooth and shiny, or any combination of these.

Explain to the children that while they are making their pet monster they should be thinking of what their monster's personality is like. The questions which you introduced at the beginning may be applied to the pet monster: 'What do you like about your pet monster? What does your pet monster like to do' and so on. Remind the children that these are domestic monsters, a tame variety, not wild monsters.

Give the children time to make their monster, and as they are working talk to them about the physical characteristics they are choosing and about the personality and behaviour of their pet monster.

When the monsters have been completed, the children should cut them out, pencil their initials on the back and leave the monsters to dry. Ask the children to think about their monster overnight, remembering what it looks like and what kind of personality it has, and to try to decide on a good name for the monster.

MONSTER NAMES

W→✝✝→✝ 20

Teaching content
Names are part of the character.

What you need
Photocopiable page 149 (the caption 'This is my pet monster _____'), Velcro strips to fit the length of each monster, A3 sugar paper, A5 paper, glue, writing materials.

What to do
Ask the children to collect their monster and bring it to the group.

Explain to them that each child is going to select a name for his or her pet monster. Discuss with them what their real-life pets are called and how the names were selected. Children may be able to provide examples from their own experience. Write up a list of pet names from those the children have given. Discuss with the children why the names are appropriate for the different types of pets and for their appearance and personality. Explain that authors have to select names for their characters too. Use some examples from familiar stories (*Blooming Cats* has a good selection). Discuss with the children why the authors may have thought these were good names for the characters in their stories.

Now ask the children for examples of some of the names they have thought of for their pet monsters. Take a few examples, each time exploring why the child thinks this will be a good name for their pet monster. Put the children into pairs and tell them that each child must take their pet monster and tell the other child the name they have chosen. If they have more than one name, or if they are not sure, the writing partner can help them to decide on one.

When they have made their final choice, they should bring the monster back to the group. Then let each child introduce the pet monster to the class or group, 'This is my pet monster...'

Give each child the caption 'This is my pet monster _____', copied and cut out from photocopiable page 149, and a sheet of A3 sugar paper. Tell them to go back to their tables and write the name of their monster in the space on the strip of paper. When they have done this they should paste it near the bottom of the page, leaving room for their monster above. Go round and help each child to attach the Velcro strip to the back of the monster and the corresponding strip to the page above the writing. The children can then stick their monsters on to the page above their monster's name.

MEET MY MONSTER
✝≠✝ ⑳

Teaching content
Rehearsing and writing character detail and personalities.

What you need
Completed monster sheet from session 2, photocopiable page 149 (the caption 'Things you need to know about my monster'), A3 sugar paper, A5 paper, glue, writing materials.

What to do
Remind the children of the things they were thinking about when they were creating their monsters (see the list of questions in session 1). Give them a few minutes to remember their ideas about their monster's appearance, behaviour and personality. Now pair them with their writing partners and explain that each child has to take it in turn to tell the other all about their monster. If they wish, they could think about what they would need to tell their partner if he or she were going to look after the monster overnight or during the holidays.

When the children have had time to introduce their monsters, ask them to write out a description of their pet, giving it a heading: 'Things you need to know about my monster', copied and cut out from photocopiable page 149. When the children have finished writing, tell them to paste their heading in the middle of the A3 sugar paper at the top and then paste their writing below.

4

THE DAY MY MONSTER CAME TO SCHOOL – THE PLAYGROUND

✝ ⏱30

Teaching content

Sequencing and structuring the story by introducing unusual events.

What you need

Completed A3 sheet from session 3, photocopiable page 149 (the caption 'One day my pet monster came to school. When he arrived at the school gate...'), photocopiable pages 69 and 151, Velcro strip to correspond to 'monster' strip, A3 sugar paper, A5 paper folded into quarters to create four boxes, plain A5 paper, glue, writing and drawing materials.

What to do

Tell the children to turn over the sugar paper with the writing on it from session 3, then to paste the velcro strip in the middle of the page and attach their monster. Explain to the children that one day the monster wanted to go to school. Give them the caption cut out from a copy of photocopiable page 149 and tell them to paste this under the monster. Ask them to imagine that one morning when they were standing in the playground waiting to go into class they saw a monster arriving at the school gate. How would they react? What would they do? What kinds of expression would they have on their faces? What would they be saying?

Now give the children the four-box sheet and ask them to draw someone they know in the class or in the school in each box. Tell the children that you would like them to draw the people as they looked when they reacted to seeing a monster arriving at the school gate. Some of the children might be saying something, or crying or shouting. Give each child two speech bubbles (from page 69) and ask them to write in them what two children were saying.

When all of the drawings have been made, tell the children to cut them out and paste them separately on the left-hand side of the next A3 sheet of sugar paper (or paste the whole sheet without cutting out the pictures). Then the speech bubbles can be pasted near the appropriate drawings.

Now give the children some A5 paper, one sheet each, and ask them to write a description of what all the children did when the monster arrived at the school gate, then to paste their writing beside the drawings.

Finally, give each child a picture of the school gates cut out from a copy of photocopiable page 151. This should be pasted down the left-hand side and stuck to the left-hand side of the A3 sheet so that it covers the drawings of the children.

When the pages are dry, store them in the children's writing folders.

5

THE DAY MY MONSTER CAME TO SCHOOL – THE CLASSROOM

✝ ⏱20

Teaching content

Sequencing and structuring the story by introducing unusual events.

What you need

Completed A3 sheet from session 4, photocopiable page 149 (the caption 'When my monster came into the classroom...'), photocopiable page 69 (optional), Velcro strip, A3 sugar paper, A5 paper, glue, writing and drawing materials.

Ask the children to take out the completed sheet from session 4. Tell them to turn it over and to paste on the Velcro strip. Now they can put their monster in place. Explain to the children that the monster followed everyone else into the classroom. Give them the caption cut out from a copy of photocopiable page 149 to paste under the monster.

Now discuss with the children how the teacher would react if a monster came into the classroom? What would she say? What would she do? What kind of expression would be on her face? Take some suggestions from the children, but stress that they can all decide what they think the teacher would do. Give each child a sheet of A5 paper and explain that you would like them to draw a picture of the teacher when she sees the monster in the classroom. Remind the children to fill most of the page with their drawing.

When the drawing has been completed, ask the children to write down how the teacher reacted, on a sheet of A5 paper. If the children wish, they can also make speech bubbles of what the teacher said or shrieked!

When all the parts are ready, they should be pasted on the next piece of A3 sugar paper. When dry, it should be stored in the writer's folder.

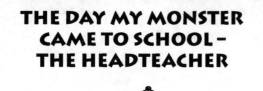

THE DAY MY MONSTER CAME TO SCHOOL – THE HEADTEACHER

✝ ⏲20

Teaching content
Sequencing and structuring the story by introducing unusual events.

What you need
Completed A3 sheet from session 5, photocopiable page 150 (The caption 'My monster ran out of the classroom and down the corridor and bumped into the headteacher'), Velcro strip, A5 paper, glue, writing and drawing materials.

Tell the children to take out the completed sheet from the previous session and to turn it over, sticking on the Velcro strip. They can then put their monster in place. Explain to the children that the monster decided to explore the school, so it went out of the classroom and along the corridor where it bumped into the headteacher. Give them the caption cut out from a copy of photocopiable page 150 and tell them to paste it below their monster.

Discuss with the children what would happen if a large pet monster was running and bumped into someone. Ask the children to draw a picture of the headteacher after the bump with the monster, using A5 paper. On a separate A5 sheet they should describe what happened.

When all the parts are ready, tell the children to paste them on to the next piece of A3 sugar paper. When dry, it should be stored in the writer's folder.

Scholastic
IMAGINATIVE WRITING
Workshop

7

RESCUE

† ⏱20

Teaching content

The ending to the story must resolve the events in a way that is satisfactory to the reader.

What you need

Completed A3 sheet from session 6, photocopiable page 150 (the caption 'I knew my pet monster had been frightened by the children, the teacher and the headteacher so I decided to...'), Velcro strip, A3 sugar paper, A5 paper, glue, writing and drawing materials.

What to do

Ask the children to take out the completed sheet from session 6. Tell them to turn it over and to stick on the Velcro strip. Now they can put their monster in place. Remind them that this is their pet monster who is really quite tame and lovable and that as its owner each child will have to think of a way to rescue their pet monster from the situation it has created in the school. Give them the caption cut out from a copy of photocopiable page 150 and ask them to paste it on.

Then give each child a thinking sheet for noting down their ideas about how to rescue their pet monster. They can make small drawings or notes. Comment on suggestions and offer support and advice. Ask the children to draw a picture of the rescue on an A5 sheet. Then ask them to write on another A5 sheet about how they rescued their pet monster. They should paste the drawing and the writing on the next piece of sugar paper. When dry, it should be stored in the writer's folder.

8

THE END

† ⏱20

Teaching content

Ending the story with the main character's reflection on events is one concluding strategy used by authors; sequencing the story and constructing the book.

What you need

Completed writing from session 7, photocopiable page 150 (with title caption 'Meet my monster'), Velcro strip, A3 sugar paper, strip of paper, glue, stapler, writing and drawing materials.

What to do

After the children have taken out the completed sheet from the previous session, tell them to turn it over and to stick on the Velcro strip. Now they can put their monster in place. Remind the children that the monster has been rescued from the school. Explain that a final sentence is required to end the story. This should depict how the monster felt after being rescued from the school. Discuss with the children what the monster might be thinking and what it would be glad to be doing now that it has been rescued from the school. Give them a few minutes to write their ending on a strip of paper. You can circulate to offer advice and support. Tell the children to paste the final piece of writing underneath the monster.

Now ask the children to lay out all their pages in sequence from the start of the story to

the end. Give the children a blank piece of A3 sugar paper for the back cover. Tell them to put this down on the table and starting from the end of the story to place the other pages on top. Give each child a blank piece of A3 sugar paper for the front cover. Check that all the children have their pages in order, then staple them along the left-hand side to make the book. Tell the children to stick the Velcro strip in the middle of the cover and then attach the monster. Then give the children the caption which provides the title cut out from a copy of photocopiable page 150 and ask them to paste it above the monster. Underneath the monster they should write their name, using thick felt-tipped pens in different colours.

Now that the book is ready, the children can try out how it works by moving their monster from page to page and reading the story.

CELEBRATION AND REVIEW

Teaching content

Sharing their book with a reader and receiving comments on specific aspects of the story helps writers to recognise what is good in their writing and reinforces their identity as authors.

What you need

Completed story books, photocopiable page 152, reading partner from a class of older children.

What to do

If possible, before undertaking this session you should link with a teacher of older children in the school and invite her and her class to participate. Arrange suitable pairings of younger and older children. Ask the invited teacher to prepare her class to be good listeners and to be encouraging to the young writers. They should be briefed on their role as evaluators and have time to familiarise themselves with the evaluation questions.

On the day of the session, the older children should come, a few at a time, to hear the children's stories. Then they should complete the evaluation sheet and discuss its contents with the writer of the story. The writer should thank the older child and then file the evaluation sheet in his or her writer's folder.

The headteacher may be very interested in the stories and at a suitable time could visit the children to see the completed books and listen to the stories.

Display the children's books in a prominent position and give the children the opportunity to look at the different versions.

Further development

The monsters might go to other places: the supermarket, the park, or on holiday.

MAKING MY MONSTER

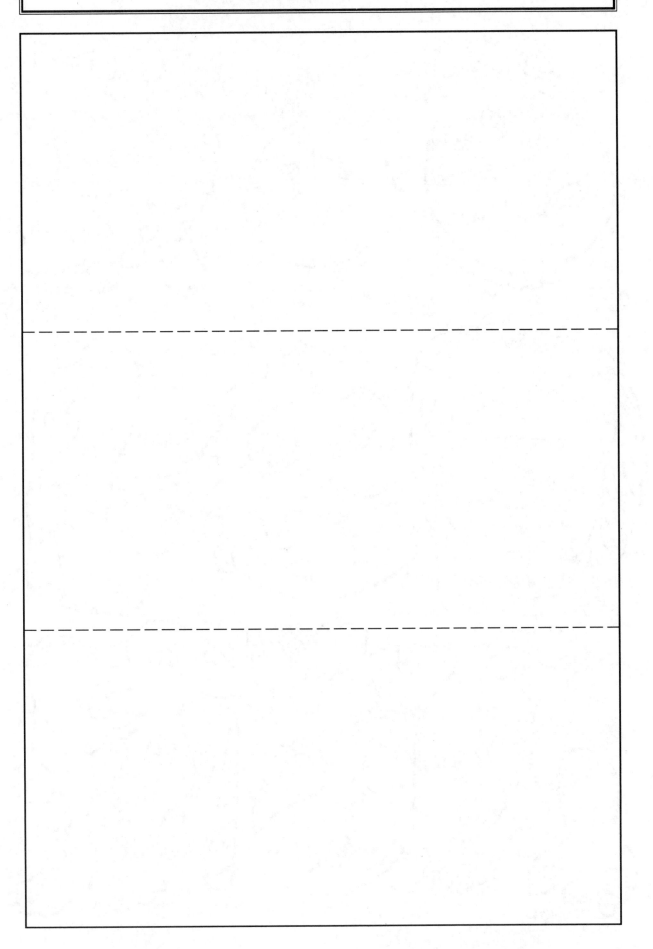

MONSTER PARTS

Scholastic
IMAGINATIVE WRITING
Workshop

CAPTIONS

This is my pet monster _____

Things you need to know about my monster

One day my pet monster came to school. When he arrived at the school gate...

When my monster came into the classroom...

CAPTIONS

My monster ran out of the classroom, down the corridor and bumped into the headteacher.

I knew my pet monster had been frightened by the children, the teacher and the headteacher so I decided to...

MEET MY MONSTER

THE SCHOOL GATES

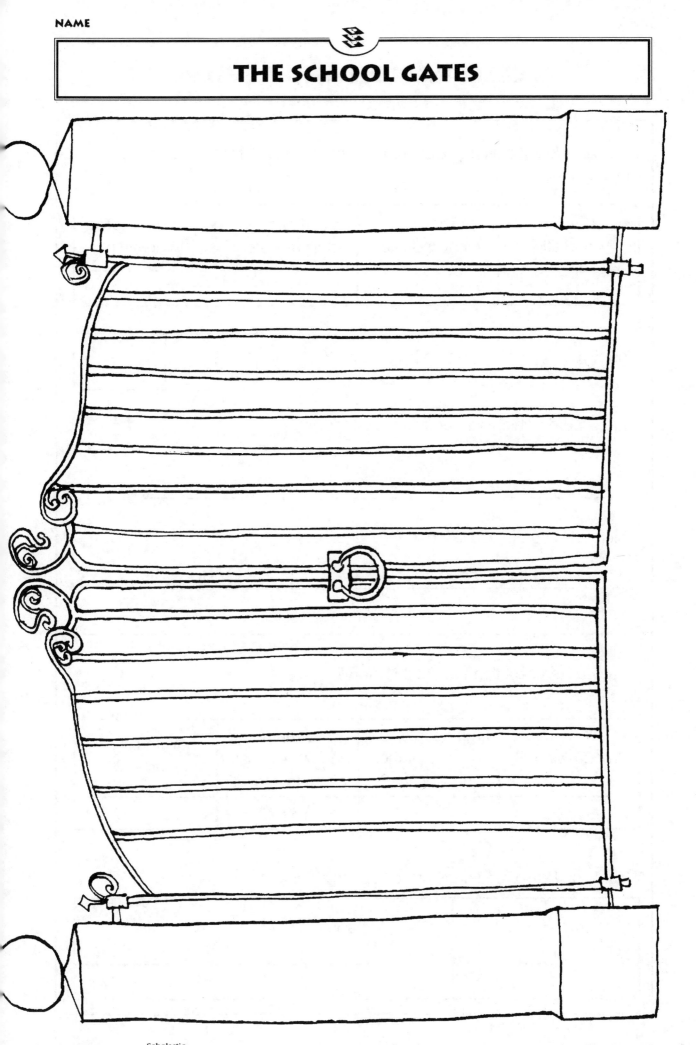

CELEBRATION AND REVIEW

What was your first impression from the front cover? Tick the box.
Did you think

That's a good title	That's a funny monster	I wish I had made this monster	This book looks interesting

Would you like the monster to be your pet?

Yes	No

Write 3 words which sum up this monster?

_____   _____   _____

Which drawing did you like best?

_____

_____

What was the best thing about this story?
Was it

the drawings?	what people said when they met the monster?	what happened when the monster came to school?	how the story ended?

Would you like to read another book by this author?

Yes, very much	Perhaps	Not really